HOM.

TERENCE BLACKER

Resource Material
Rachel O'Neill

Series Consultant
Cecily O'Neill

Collins Educational
An imprint of HarperCollins*Publishers*

Published by Collins Educational
77–85 Fulham Palace Road, London W6 8JB
An imprint of HarperCollins*Publishers*

© Copyright 1994 playscript Terence Blacker, resource material
HarperCollins*Publishers*

First published 1994

ISBN 0003303071

Acknowledgements

The following permissions to reproduce material are gratefully
acknowledged:
Text extracts: from *Homebird* (the novel) by Terence Blacker, Piccadilly
Press, 1991, pp. 33–34, 48–49; from *A Cry from the Streets* by Frank
Dawes, Wayland Publishers, pp. 58–60; from *A Day to Remember*,
Centrepoint Soho, pp. 61–62; 'Tramps on Waterloo Station' by Robert
Morgan, p. 64; 'The City' by John Betjeman, John Murray Publishers
Ltd, p. 65; 'The Great Escape' by Damon Syson, The *Guardian*,
pp. 66–69; 'Runaways' from The NCH Factfile, p. 70–71.
Illustrations: Dover Books, pp. 56, 57; The Dickens House Museum,
London, pp. 47, 52; Gay Galsworthy, pp. 31, 36, 55; Peter Grant, p. 63;
Crispin Hughes (Photofusion), pp. 44, 45; The Mansell Collection, p. 39;
J Southworth (Photofusion), p. 67; Bob Watkins (Photofusion), pp. 42,
59.

Design by Wendi Watson
Cover design by Chi Leung
Cover photograph by Bob Watkins (Photofusion)

Commissioning Editor: Domenica de Rosa
Editor: Rebecca Lloyd
Production: James Graves

Typeset in Linotron Century Schoolbook by
Northern Phototypesetting Co Ltd, Bolton
Printed and bound in Great Britain
by Scotprint, Musselburgh

CONTENTS

BACKGROUND TO THE PLAY

I first wrote *Homebird* as a novel. It was a story in which I wanted to show a thirteen-year-old boy on a dramatic collision course with the adult world, cut off from the securities of a comfortable home life, on a personal journey of escape – and discovery. I tried to make it exciting, sometimes funny and occasionally moving.

In other words, *Homebird* was written primarily as an entertainment.

Yet, often when you write a story, themes and ideas are bubbling away beneath the surface without your knowing it. Adapting *Homebird* as a play, I became aware that, between the lines of the story, I had been exploring some particular concerns.

One was the idea of home. The progress of Nicky Morrison, the hero of the story, sees him moving from a suburban family home to the institutionalised home of a boarding-school, then to the rough, lawless home of a teenage squat, and ending up in the cruellest home of all – Cardboard City.

In each of these places, Nicky has to come to terms with different kinds of authority. At home, a fog of self-deception, the rule of 'parents-know-best', hides real pain and problems.

Questions aren't encouraged either at Holton College where school rules ensure an unchallenged hierarchy. The command structure at the squat, under the fearsome rule of Scag, is enforced by a more open kind of violence. Finally, on the streets, Nicky enters a bewildering twilight world where any kind of communication is hedged by paranoia and fear.

Nicky experiences all this when he's at a difficult age, caught between the securities of childhood and the desire to stand up for himself as a near-adult. Decisions – which school to attend, for example – are still being made on his behalf and, when he decides to take action, his views and needs tend to be ignored. After all, he's just a kid.

But, by the end of *Homebird*, Nicky Morrison has come

through. He has taken responsibility for his life, and has reached people – family and strangers – who once would have taken him for granted. He has found his own kind of power and independence.

There are other themes in *Homebird* – teenage runaways, homelessness, bullying, the family – but the main story is about a thirteen-year-old boy who takes on the adult world, and survives.

Terence Blacker

THE CHARACTERS

NICKY MORRISON – a thirteen-year-old boy
MRS MORRISON – his mother
MR MORRISON – his father
BETH MORRISON – his older sister
PAUL – a school friend
QUADIR – another school friend
PRINGLE – an older school bully
MISS DOVER – the school nurse
JO – Mr Morrison's secretary
MARLON – an old friend of Nicky's
SCAG – A teenage car thief
CARLA – Marlon's sister and Scag's girlfriend
PETE – a teenage squatter
JULIE – another teenage squatter
OLD WOMAN – a citizen of Cardboard City
FIRST HOMELESS TEENAGER
SECOND HOMELESS TEENAGER

WAITER
FEMALE COMMUTER
MALE COMMUTER
HOMELESS MAN
FIRST POLICEMAN
SECOND POLICEMAN
JESSIE – a small dog

The following parts can be doubled up:
PAUL and **HOMELESS TEENAGER**
PRINGLE and **HOMELESS TEENAGER**
MISS DOVER and **OLD WOMAN**
JO, FEMALE COMMUTER and **HOMELESS TEENAGER**
MARLON and **FIRST POLICEMAN**
WAITER, MALE COMMUTER and **SECOND POLICEMAN**

The size of the cast, with this doubling up, will be fifteen – and a dog.

vi

ACT ONE

*A dark stage, except for a spotlight, stage left. **Nicky** sits up suddenly, as if waking from a nightmare. His head is illuminated by the spotlight.*

NICKY   Easy, tiger.

He relaxes as he realizes where he is.

Sometimes, when I wake at the dead of night, the memories are there, so close that I could reach out and touch them. The purple rhododendrons outside my new school. A shadowy figure on a rooftop, half lit by a flashing blue light. My father looking for me, his eyes haunted and vacant.

All just a year ago. When I was thirteen.

Then the sounds crowd in on me – voices, a police siren getting nearer and nearer and I'm running, my breath sobbing in my chest and – *easy*, tiger.

When you're fourteen, you can't cry out in the middle of the night. It's like just not done.

So I lie here – alone with my memories . . .

*The stage lights up to reveal, stage right, **Nicky's** mother, **Mrs Mary Morrison**, a woman in her early forties. She's in a kitchen. She's putting candles in a cake, laying the table, singing along to a radio that's playing the old song 'Our House' by Crosby, Stills, Nash and Young. Behind her, sprawled in a seat, her face obscured by a magazine, is **Beth, Nicky's** older sister, who's sixteen, slightly plump and moody.*

Nicky *stands up and watches his mother for a moment. He's in his school clothes.*

NICKY   *to the audience* My thirteenth birthday, the glorious dawning of my teenage years. School's over and I'm in for like the biggest surprise of my entire life. *He walks towards the kitchen, chucking his satchel on the floor as he goes.* Hi, Mum. Thanks for putting balloons on the front door. Like

1

embarrass me in front of the entire neighbourhood, right? *He kisses her.*

MRS MORRISON *turning off the radio* It's not *like* embarrass you, Nicky. And you don't have to end every sentence with 'right'.

NICKY No. If you'd put up a sign saying 'THIRTEEN TODAY – HAPPY BIRTHDAY, MY DARLING NICKY' – that would have embarrassed me. A couple of balloons is just *like* embarrassing . . . Right? *Mrs Morrison laughs. Nicky picks a label off the side of the cake.* Thanks for baking a cake, Mum. You shouldn't have bothered.

BETH *from behind the magazine* Sarcasm is the lowest form of wit.

NICKY *to the audience* My sister Beth – undisputed queen of the totally obvious cliché.

BETH Anyway it's the thought that counts, isn't it?

Nicky gives the audience a see-what-I-mean look.

MRS MORRISON There. *She steps back from the cake and looks at it.* Dad'll be home soon.

NICKY Dad?

MRS MORRISON He's bringing your present.

NICKY But it's only four o'clock.

BETH Knock me down with a feather.

NICKY I mean, isn't he missing two hours of precious office time?

MRS MORRISON Don't be rude about your father, Nicky.

NICKY Come on, Mum. It's you who's always going on about him being married to his job.

MRS MORRISON It's your birthday.

NICKY Last year he didn't get back until eight o'clock. It was all, 'Sorry old boy, couldn't get away from the damned meeting'.

MRS MORRISON Well, this year he wants to – *She stops, not wanting to say too much. Beth lowers her magazine.*

NICKY Yeah?

MRS MORRISON This birthday's special . . . different.

Nicky is still unconvinced. We hear the sounds of a key unlocking the front door, centre stage. Moments later, Mr

2

Morrison, a brisk, middle-aged man in a business suit, enters. In one hand he has a briefcase. In the other, a lead attached to a small dog. Nicky gasps and kneels in front of the dog.

NICKY I don't believe it.

MR MORRISON This is Jessie. Happy birthday, old boy.

NICKY It's a dog.

BETH Man's best friend.

NICKY Tell me I'm not dreaming. *Mr and Mrs Morrison exchange glances. Nicky looks up now sensing an odd atmosphere.* I don't know what to say. *Mrs Morrison turns away as if to hide tears.* All right. What's going on?

MR MORRISON We need to talk, old boy. *Awkwardly, he puts an arm round Nicky's neck and leads him to the table. They both sit down.* Today you're a teenager. I feel – we both feel – it's an excellent time to take stock of the situation.

NICKY *suspiciously* Situation?

MR MORRISON School.

NICKY *groaning* It's my birthday.

There's something prepared about the following speech, as if Mr Morrison has rehearsed it many times.

MR MORRISON We both feel you're old enough to take more responsibility for your schooling. As you know, your reports have been a bitter disappointment recently. Every subject was the same. Lazy. Lack of interest. Could try harder. Messes about in lessons.

NICKY It was better last term. I was almost in the middle of the class.

MR MORRISON Middle.

NICKY Yeah, average. What's wrong with that?

MR MORRISON *becoming more heated* I'll tell you what's wrong with average. Average means leaving school with no A Levels. Average means a place at the back of the dole queue.

NICKY But that's what I am, don't you understand? I'm just . . . middle, average, ordinary. Someone's got to be average, haven't they? Otherwise it wouldn't be average.

MR MORRISON *refusing to be drawn into an argument* There's no place for average in this day and age.

BETH It's a jungle out there. *They all freeze her with a look.* Well, it is.

3

MRS MORRISON We want better for you, Nicky.

MR MORRISON So we've been looking at Holton.

NICKY Holton? The school you went to? But it's –

MRS MORRISON *clearly less convinced about all this than her husband* It's for the best, Nicky.

NICKY But it's a private school.

MR MORRISON Completely changed since my day. Computers. Girls in the sixth form, the lot.

NICKY It's –

MRS MORRISON It's not at all how you think, Nicky.

NICKY It's a boarding-school, Mum.

MR MORRISON At Holton, you'll learn to stand on your own two feet, live in the real world. You'll get away from *He glances at **Mrs Morrison*** apron strings.

MRS MORRISON *reacting angrily* That was unnecessary, Gordon. Were *you* living in the real world at his age?

MR MORRISON Well at least I had interests. I wanted to get on with life.

MRS MORRISON *sarcastically* Ah yes of course – Holton made you the man you are.

MR MORRISON And what exactly is that supposed to mean?

MRS MORRISON You know perfectly well what –

NICKY *heading off the row with an interruption* When? *It works – his parents pull themselves together.* When do I go?

MRS MORRISON September.

MR MORRISON It will change everything, old boy. Give you a bit of independence.

NICKY *laughing ruefully* Independence. Like kick me out of the house. So that's why I get a dog at last. Sugar the pill, right?

MR MORRISON *awkwardly tender* I had a wonderful time there. It helped me a lot later in life.

NICKY *looking at him coldly* Great recommendation, Dad. *He gives Jessie's lead to **Mrs Morrison*** You can keep Jessie. I won't be seeing much of her, will I?

*Nicky walks out of the kitchen, which goes into darkness. **Mr** and **Mrs Morrison** and **Beth** leave stage right. Slowly, he walks over to a hatrack at the back of the stage, takes off his scruffy black*

4

blazer and school tie, puts on a new school tie and tweed coat that were hanging up – he is now a public schoolboy.

NICKY *to the audience* So. Holton College. Six months later. Some arguments you can't win, yeah? Think rhododendron bushes. Think huge, well-tended lawns where no one's allowed to walk. Think like a million light years away from the real world. At Holton, everything normal's turned upside down. You arrive and they call you a new man. When you leave, you're an old boy. There are rules for pretty much everything, but, basically, when you're a new man, there are just four big unwritten rules. Rule One: Do not do anything that will get you noticed by anyone bigger than you. Rule Two: Do not speak unless spoken to. Rule Three: Do not answer back if one of the seniors asks you to do something, however sad and ridiculous it might be.

He's interrupted by a bellow from backstage.

The voice of PRINGLE: Quadir!

NICKY And Rule Four: Keep clear of Pringle.

PRINGLE *more loudly, still backstage* Quadir!

Nicky walks stage right and, as the right-hand side of the stage is lit up, we see that there's now an iron bed and two chairs. Quadir, an owlish Asian boy, is reading a book on the bed. Paul is sitting on a chair, playing a mini-computer game. Both are about Nicky's age.

NICKY *Still to the audience* My dorm. That's Paul. And this is Quadir – like, a death wish on legs.

Pringle, an older boy with angry spots, bursts in. He's carrying a pair of shoes. Nicky sits on the other chair.

PRINGLE Are you deaf, Ali Baba?

QUADIR *with dignity* The name's Quadir.

Pringle throws the shoes on the floor by the bed Clean them, boy.

QUADIR My parents told me there was no fagging at Holton.

PRINGLE Your parents? I don't see any parents round here.

QUADIR They said –

PRINGLE If those shoes aren't shining in two minutes, I'll just have to do your face some serious harm. Comprende? *He storms out. Quadir goes back to reading his book. There's an*

5

awkward silence.

PAUL   Quadir.

QUADIR   *as if nothing has happened*   Hmm?

NICKY   Just do it, Quadir.

QUADIR   My parents were definitely told that there was no fagging.

NICKY   Don't you understand? The guy's a psycho. He won't just make *your* life hell – it'll be all of us. It doesn't matter what anyone tells your parents. This is just between Pringle and us.

QUADIR   It's the principle that counts.   *Paul angrily picks up the shoes and begins to polish them.*   I'll ring my parents.

NICKY   Don't. Anyway we're not allowed to ring home for the first three weeks. You know that.   *As **Paul** polishes and **Quadir** reads, **Nicky** takes a writing pad from a desk.*

PAUL   You're an idiot, Quadir.

NICKY   *as he writes on the pad*   Dear Mum and Dad, How are you? How's Jessie? How's my bedroom? How's the house? How are Jody, Ben, Ellie, Marlon and all my friends from school? How's Mr Harrington next door? How's Mr Harrington's tortoise? How's the newsagent where I used to get sweets? How's London? I'm OK, I suppose. Love Nicky – your son in case you've forgotten. PS How's Beth?

PAUL   *sarcastically putting the shoes, now polished, on **Quadir's** bed*   Next time you're on your own, guy.

QUADIR   *looking up*   You just don't see it, do you? If you'd been born like me, you'd understand. Ever since I first heard human voices, it's been insults, humiliations. You try to ignore it, but then it gets worse – they push you further and further. You have to make a stand. Once you let these people know they've got the better of you –   *He stops as **Pringle** returns, **Pringle** picks up the shoes, inspects them.*

PRINGLE   Better.

There's a tense pause.

QUADIR   You can thank Paul. He did them.

PAUL   Gee thanks, Quadir.

PRINGLE   *looking, enraged, at **Paul**, then at **Nicky***   You are all dead meat in here.   *He grabs the book **Quadir** is reading.*

QUADIR   *hysterically trying to retrieve the book*   No!

6

Pringle *pushes him back onto the bed* Give me that back, Pringle – please!

PRINGLE *delighted to have upset* **Quadir** *at last* The Koran. What's that then? Some sort of porn, is it?

Nicky and Paul are now standing as Quadir lies, sobbing, on the bed.

NICKY It's his Koran, Pringle – it's his holy book.

PAUL Don't do it, Pringle. Reading that is like his way of praying.

PRINGLE Yeah, well my desk needs propping up and this is just the right size. *He leaves.*

Paul goes over to comfort Quadir.

NICKY He's not getting away with that.

PAUL What are you going to do?

NICKY Just have to go to the top, won't I? Mr Watts.

PAUL *as Nicky leaves* Mr Watts? You're mad, Nicky.

NICKY *to the audience as he makes his way stage left* He was right.

Nicky leaves stage left to see Mr Watts. After a pause, Pringle re-appears at a slow walk, mockingly carrying the book before him like a butler with a tray. He enters the dormitory. With icy sarcasm, he puts the book on Quadir's bed. Nicky follows him uncertainly. As Pringle turns to leave, he sees Nicky at the door. Without a word he raises one infinitely threatening finger, then leaves. A distant telephone sounds and keeps ringing.

PAUL Write your will.

Nicky sits down on a chair, his face in his hands. The telephone stops ringing.

VOICE *off stage* Morrison! Telephone.

Nicky stands, walks out of the dormitory to a small kiosk telephone, stage left. The receiver is resting on its side. He picks it up.

NICKY Hullo . . . Beth? You're not meant to ring here . . . No, don't worry, doesn't matter . . . What kind of emergency? . . . Look it's no good saying, 'It's not exactly all quiet on the home front' and 'Home is not sweet home' . . . What, fighting? . . . Having rows? . . . Is it worse than usual? . . . All right, all right . . . Easy, tiger, easy . . . Yeah, leave it to me. I'll think of something. Bye, Beth. *He hangs up and turns, deep in thought, to the audience.* My sister's not like the greatest of communicators, but, between the clichés, she's telling me that World War Three's breaking out at home. When I'm around, I know how to distract Mum and Dad from their rows *He makes his way slowly towards the dormitory, the audience can see **Pringle** skulking in the shadows* but Beth – *imitating her* it's a free country, isn't it. Every cloud has a silver lining. Excuse me, I only live here. Takes all sorts to make the world. *More seriously* – I have to think of – *He looks up to see **Pringle** barring his way* Ah.

PRINGLE You should never run down the corridor, Morrison.

NICKY Running? I wasn't running, Pringle.

PRINGLE Because if you run *He takes **Nicky** by the hair* you could have an accident. A very nasty accident.

NICKY Pringle, please no –

***Pringle** brings his knee up to **Nicky's** face – hard. At the moment of impact, all the stagelights go out. In the darkness, we can hear **Nicky's** moans. Gradually, stage right, a flickering light, growing stronger, picks out **Nicky** as he regains consciousness, a bandage over one eye and lying in a bed in the school sanatorium. A nurse, **Miss Dover**, is by the bed, looking down at him.*

NICKY Wh . . . where am I? What happened?

MISS DOVER You're in the san. You had an accident.

NICKY *remembering* Oh yeah, right. An accident.

MISS DOVER You'll have to be in here until the day after tomorrow.

NICKY No classes? No games?

MISS DOVER Certainly not. That's a nasty knock you've had. *As she straightens the bedclothes, **Paul** and **Quadir** appear.*

PAUL Nice one. When they take that bandage off, you'll look like the Elephant Man.

QUADIR It was Pringle, right?

NICKY Yeah.

PAUL He told Mr Watts you ran and tripped – hit your head on the doorknob.

QUADIR   I'm going to tell Watts about this. And my parents.

NICKY   *sighing*   Not exactly a fast learner, are you?

PAUL   But he's right, Nick. Pringle can't just get away with that.

NICKY   It doesn't matter. I'm outta here, guys.

PAUL   How d'you mean?

NICKY   I need my jeans, my outside clothes – and some cash.

PAUL   Don't be stupid, Nicky. You can't leg it out of here. Now that he's had his revenge, Pringle's not going to bother you any more.

NICKY   It's not Pringle. It's . . . personal. I'm checking out of the san tomorrow afternoon. Watts won't expect me until the following morning – by then I'll be in London.   *To Quadir* I'll need twenty quid minimum.

QUADIR   I'm not sure I could –

NICKY   Under your mattress, Quadir. We've seen it.

PAUL   Come on, guy. Think what Nicky's done for you.

Quadir nods reluctantly.

NICKY   Great. I need them by tomorrow afternoon.   *Paul and Quadir leave. Nicky sits up in bed and addresses the audience.*   For once Beth's cliché was right – every cloud does have a silver lining.

Change of lighting. It's the next day. Miss Dover is fussing around the bed, exuding disapproval.

MISS DOVER   I really don't know about this, Morrison. I told Mr Watts you'd be back tomorrow morning. You've only been in here twenty-four hours. Normally boys try to stay in here as long as possible.

NICKY   I must be one of the keen ones.

MISS DOVER   You must be.

Paul and Quadir enter. Miss Dover looks at them suspiciously.

PAUL   Spare clothes, Nicky.   *He gives Nicky a plastic bag.*

NICKY   Ah. Thanks.   *While Miss Dover's back is turned, Quadir slips him the money. Nicky smiles with gratitude.*   Oh well. Back to work.

Miss Dover, Paul and Quadir leave as Nicky puts on his shirt and trousers. As he addresses the audience, the lights go down, leaving the spotlight on him, centre stage.

NICKY   Or rather, back to London. Except – I've thought this one out – I'm not going home first. If Dad comes back and finds me hanging around in the kitchen, not standing on my own two feet, not living in the real world, I'll be shipped back to Holton like a convict. No, I need to catch him as he leaves the office at the end of the day, explain to him why I should be at home – like, man to man. Tactics, see.

Goodbye Holton.   *He sticks out his thumb, a hitch-hiker.* Goodbye Psycho Pringle.

To his left, offstage, a car has stopped. **Nicky** *addresses the driver.*   Yeah, London. Anywhere will do.   *With a thumbs-up to the audience,* **Nicky** *runs off stage left.*

Lights down, to suggest evening. Stage right, **Mr Morrison** *emerges, briefcase in hand, a businessman at the end of his working day. Behind him is* **Jo***, his secretary, a woman in her early twenties. As they walk extremely slowly across the stage,* **Nicky** *appears, following them.*

NICKY   *quietly to the audience*   Wonderful, eh? I've risked everything to get here, to sort things out and my dad's like being the good boss, saying goodnight to his secretary –   *At that moment* **Jo** *laughs and links her arm through* **Mr Morrison's***.*

NICKY   Come on, Dad, lose her   *He frowns as he sees his father glancing back nervously, then patting* **Jo** *gently on the bottom.* **Nicky** *reacts, appalled.*

NICKY   No!   *He crouches down as the couple enter an imaginary restaurant, stage left, and are shown to a table by a* **waiter***.* **Mr Morrison** *sits facing* **Jo** *and the audience. The* **waiter** *lights a candle between them.*

NICKY   All those late nights at the office.   *He walks slowly towards the restaurant until he's standing, centre stage, staring in.*   All that, let's feel sorry for the hard-working wage-earner.   **Mr Morrison** *is chatting away to* **Jo***, his hand on hers.*   Lies. Nothing but lies!   **Mr Morrison** *looks up and sees* **Nicky***. Incredulously, he gets to his feet like a man who has seen a ghost.* **Nicky** *walks away, slowly at first. As his father stands outside the restaurant shouting for him, he begins to run, leaving stage left.*

MR MORRISON   Nicky? Nicky, is that you? NICKY?

ACT TWO

Early morning, the next day. The sound of birdsong and distant traffic can be heard. Stage right, we see a bundle of plastic and blanketing – this is **Nicky**, *who's been sleeping rough.* **Nicky** *awakes slowly and realizes the enormity of what he has done. He shivers, huddles up in his plastic bag, then checks his watch.*

NICKY *to himself* Come on Marlon. *Sees someone offstage right* Marlon! MARLON!

Suspiciously, **Marlon**, *who's black, cool, and a mature fourteen, approaches.*

MARLON Nicky? Hey, what you doing in that bag, man? I thought you were meant to be at boarding school. *Sees* **Nicky's** *black eye* Been in a fight?

NICKY You should see the other guy. **Marlon** *doesn't laugh.* I need your help, Marl.

MARLON *sitting* OK, shoot.

NICKY You'll be late for school.

MARLON Right.

NICKY I'm on the run. Something happened at school and I had to get out of it. I went to see my dad but . . . he had other things on his mind.

MARLON How long you been on the street?

NICKY Just one night. I found this stuff on a tip and made a bed.

MARLON Check the boy scout.

They both laugh

NICKY I can't go home, Marl. I've got to find somewhere to stay *Upset.* I need . . . help.

MARLON Easy, tiger. *He smiles.* Nicky Morrison on the street – who'd have believed it? *He gets to his feet.*

NICKY What are we going to do?

MARLON Dump your camp bed, man – you won't need it.

NICKY *scrambling to his feet and collecting up his bedding* Where are we going, Marl?

MARLON Let's get some breakfast. You look hungry.

NICKY Breakfast? You'll be *really* late for school.

11

MARLON Right.

They both exit stage right.

Stage left is illuminated. It's the kitchen of a squat. Facing us is a wall with graffiti written on it. To the right of the front door is a window which has been partly boarded up. On the left of the room is a door leading to **Carla** *and* **Scag's** *bedroom. Front stage left is an old mattress on which* **Nicky** *will sleep. As the lights go up* **Pete** *and* **Julie**, *two young teenage squatters, are playing cards on a battered sofa to the right of the room. Somewhere in the squat a radio is playing 'The House of Fun' by Madness. There's a knock at the door.* **Pete** *and* **Julie** *ignore it. Another knock.*

PETE Naff off.

Another, more urgent, knock. **Julie** *gets up reluctantly and looks through the slats of the window.*

JULIE It's some kid. *Through the window* Yeah?

NICKY *offstage, talking through the window* I'm looking for Carla.

JULIE No Carla here.

NICKY Tell her that Marlon sent me.

JULIE Marlon who?

NICKY Her brother.

JULIE Carla! Your brother's sent some kid round for you. *She knocks on Carla's door.* Carla! *She goes back to the sofa.*

Carla *emerges from the bedroom sleepily. She's about fifteen and in a long T-shirt.*

CARLA My brother? What time is it?

PETE Too bloomin' early for callers. Eleven or something.

Carla *unlocks the door, which has several bolts on it.* **Nicky** *is standing on the doorstep.*

CARLA Now what's little Marlon been up to?

NICKY My name's Nicky Morrison. He asked me to give you this. *He gives her a note.*

CARLA *coming back into the room* Nicky Morrison? Weren't you at school with him? Come in anyway. *Reads the note as* **Nicky** *enters.* Ah. You're on the street. **Pete** *and* **Julie** *register interest.*

12

NICKY Yeah. Marlon said you could help.

CARLA He did, did he? Coffee? *She gives two dirty cups a rough wipe with a cloth.*

NICKY Please.

CARLA *as she makes coffee* I can see the running away from school. But what's wrong with home?

NICKY There are problems there. My parents . . . aren't getting on.

CARLA What?

NICKY I think it's serious. It could be divorce. *Pete and Julie laugh contemptuously at the triviality of his problem.* I saw my dad with his secretary. *They laugh even more.*

PETE Lose him, Carla.

JULIE Oh no, divorce, daddy with his secretary. What will they be saying down at the golf course?

NICKY It's not like that.

PETE You're in the big playground now, boy. The reason that front door's bolted is that we could get thrown out any day by the Old Bill – having been given a good kicking first. Go home to Mummy and Daddy. I'm sure they've made up their little tiff.

JULIE D'you know why I'm here? Because my mum threw me out on the street. Pete's been on the run from the police since he was twelve.

Nicky looks interrogatively at Carla.

CARLA I just . . . preferred to live away from home.

PETE And with Scag.

CARLA All right, you can stay tonight – I'll show you where to sleep.

NICKY What's Scag?

JULIE He's not going to like it.

Carla shows Nicky to a mattress, front-stage left, slightly away from the kitchen.

NICKY Who's this Scag? Who won't like it?

CARLA Scag's my boyfriend. You'll meet him later. Most days he doesn't get up until it's dark.

NICKY What is he – like Dracula?

CARLA *laughing* Yeah, but without Dracula's sense of fun.

*She returns to the kitchen where, half lit, she finishes her coffee with **Pete** and **Julie**, as **Nicky** talks to the audience.*

NICKY   *on the mattress*   I'm thinking what am I *doing* here? Me, Nicky Morrison, in a squat in South London. A week I'll give it. Then perhaps Dad will have spoken to Mum, and they'll have both decided to work it out. Or maybe I'll be able to see Dad, talk to him man to man   *Nicky acts out this scene, playing the parts of both himself and his father.*   Now listen, Dad, you know why I did what I did – I'll say nothing to Mum if you stop treating her like that. Understand?   *As his father*   That's very decent of you, old boy.   *As himself*   Don't give me that old boy routine, Dad. I'll come home if you spend more time with Mum. And fire that secretary. That's the deal, right?   *As his father*   It's a deal, Nick. Now about school –   *Interrupting as himself*   What about school?   *As his father*   Er, nothing. What would *you* like to do about school, old boy?   *Nicky smiles to himself. He leans back against the wall, tired. He closes his eyes.*

PETE   *as the kitchen lights up*   No!   *He bangs the table.*

Nicky's eyes open as he hears the raised voices from the kitchen.

PETE   We've got enough trouble without that little toerag hanging round the place.

CARLA   Oh yeah. You own the place, do you? You're in charge, are you, Pete?

JULIE   Listen, I'm sure he's a nice enough kid but, let's face it, he's just a boy from the suburbs who's had a barney with his mum and dad.

PETE   Don't you see, Carla? People like us are invisible. Our families gave up on us years ago but him – his parents will get the police involved. He'll get spotted and lead them straight back here.

CARLA   So we keep him hidden for a while.

JULIE   Eating our food, right? I thought the idea of this squat was that everyone should bring some money in –

Nicky gets up from the mattress and walks slowly towards the kitchen.

PETE   What's he good for, this kid? Thieving? Hustling? What's the use of him?

NICKY   I've got some money.   *They all look at him as he*

14

walks forward, reaches into his pocket and puts some money on the table. Six pounds ninety.

JULIE Oh, wonderful.

Pete reaches for the money, but Carla grabs it first and gives it back to Nicky.

CARLA Keep it. You'll need it.

Pete and Julie react angrily.

PETE What? Why should we pay for his food?

JULIE You've gone too far this time, Carla – I'm telling Scag.

The door to Scag and Carla's bedroom opens. Scag – good-looking, charismatic, dangerous, slightly older than the others – stands there. He's not pleased at having been woken up.

SCAG Tell Scag what? What's going on?

CARLA This is Nick. He's a friend of my brother. He's on the street.

SCAG Hullo, Nick.

NICKY Hi . . . Scag.

SCAG So what's the problem then?

PETE He's got no money. We just thought it was a bit out of order.

SCAG Ever earnt any money, Nick?

NICKY I did a newsround once. *Pete snickers, but is silenced by a look from Scag.* I'm a quick learner.

SCAG Can you climb?

NICKY Climb? Yeah.

SCAG We start at one.

NICKY Right, I'll get ready.

SCAG Not now. One in the morning. Carl? *He nods in the direction of the bedroom and goes there himself. Carla follows, darting a smile in Nicky's direction.*

NICKY In the *morning*? That's when he starts work?

JULIE Yeah, and I'll tell you one thing, kid. It's not a newsround.

The stage goes dark. After a few seconds, it's half lit in the eerie neon light of the dead of night. There's a distant hum of traffic, and the following sequence has the feel of a dream to it. Scag enters with Nicky from stage right. They walk easily, naturally,

Scag all the time glancing down as if to check cars as they walk by them. Having prowled the stage for a while, they arrive at a wall with a small window about ten foot off the ground. Scag looks about, points to the window and then at Nicky. Nicky climbs on Scag's shoulders and, with some difficulty, squeezes through the window and drops to the other side. From backstage there's the sound of a chain, then a bolt being pulled back. Scag, let in by Nicky, darts off-stage, rear stage right. Seconds later, Nicky is outside the door, keeping watch.

NICKY *in an incredulous whisper* Hot wire. A BMW! Sheesh! *From backstage, the roar of a car engine being started* He did it! *Nicky runs backstage and we hear the sound of a car being driven off.*

Back in the kitchen at the squat. Carla is sitting at the kitchen table, reading a book. Scag and Nicky enter. Scag has oil on his hands, Nicky a tear down the back of his shirt, which is slightly marked by blood.

CARLA So?

Scag goes to the fridge, takes out two cans of beer, and gives one to Nicky.

SCAG A natural. Small. Athletic. Quiet. Doesn't bottle it. Doesn't talk. He'll do.

CARLA Well I never. Nick, the car thief.

NICKY *smiling* Right.

SCAG Others working, are they?

CARLA Yeah.

Scag stands up.

SCAG I've got to make a call. I'll catch you later. Oh – *He takes out a roll of notes and peels off one for Nicky.* There you go, partner. *He leaves.*

NICKY *as he pockets the money* Bit late for a call, isn't it?

CARLA That's Scag for you. Man of secrets. He has a car to sell.

Nicky swigs at the beer and tries to conceal the fact that he doesn't like it.

NICKY What do they do? The others.

CARLA You don't want to know.

NICKY Come on, Carla. They know about me.

CARLA They're in the buying and selling business. Drugs.

NICKY *trying not to be shocked* Ah. Right. Aren't they . . . a bit young?

Carla gets up to put her mug in the sink.

CARLA Only in years. *She sees Nicky's torn shirt.* What's up with your back?

NICKY Caught it on a nail when I was climbing into the depot. *He winces as Carla peels back some of the torn T-shirt.* It'll be all right.

CARLA You reckon? Go and take it off. I'll be along in a minute.

Nicky goes to his bedroom and, facing the audience, carefully takes off his T-shirt. Carla goes into her bedroom and re-appears with a small tin box and a black T-shirt.

CARLA Carla Nightingale.

NICKY A first-aid box? Some squatter you turn out to be.

CARLA *kneeling on the mattress behind him* Someone's got to be organized round here. *She puts her left hand on his shoulder as she applies the antiseptic with her right.* Now keep still. *Nicky squirms a bit, then laughs.* When are you going to call home?

NICKY Soon. Maybe tomorrow.

CARLA They'll be worried about you.

NICKY Yes. I keep having this sort of totally idealized picture of life at home – how it should be but never is . . . Dad's playing cricket with me in the back garden . . . Mum's humming some old sixties song as she picks some flowers . . . and Jessie – Jessie's playing with my sister Beth . . . I haven't seen Beth laugh like that since –

CARLA Who's Jessie?

NICKY My dog. She's a little terrier – I got her for my last birthday.

CARLA Oh no, a dog! I've always wanted a dog of my own.

NICKY She's great, you'd love her, Carla. Maybe you could come home and see her when . . . *Smiles, embarrassed at having given so much away.* Yeah, well anyway.

CARLA Don't get used to this. Nicky. It's exciting now but it's

17

hard, living on the outside. You've got something none of the rest of us has – a family that loves you. You don't want to throw it away. *Although she's finished treating* **Nicky's** *back,* **Carla's** *hand has remained on his shoulder.*

NICKY   Don't you like me being here?

CARLA   Course I do. Very much. *As she's speaking,* **Scag** *enters through the front door and stands for a moment, watching them both* It's just that I don't think you belong. Deep down, you're a homebird. *Gently she prods his back with her right hand.* Eh?

NICKY   *squirming* Ah! *They laugh together, a moment of intimacy.* **Scag** *has seen enough and walks to his bedroom. As the door slams,* **Carla** *reacts guiltily, quickly taking her hand away from* **Nicky's** *shoulder, and they both stop laughing. She stands up.* I left you one of my T-shirts. You can borrow it. *She leaves quickly and goes to her bedroom.*

Nicky slowly picks up the T-shirt and buries his face in it. After a few moments he lays it down and walks slowly centre-stage. The lights fade so that when he begins to speak he's in a solitary spotlight.

NICKY   So a week passes like it's a day. I get into the rhythm of the squat – go to bed when other people are going to work, get up after lunch, work every night with Scag. But something's changed. There's like an atmosphere, yeah?

Backstage left, a second spotlight picks up **Pete** *during his speech, then goes dark.*

PETE   You think you're in, don't you? You're nothing, guy. You're history. Just wait and see.

NICKY   *to the audience* But I don't see it, I'm working all right. I'm paying for my food. The police aren't exactly breaking down the door to find me.

JULIE   *spotlight, front stage left* Quite the little innocent, aren't we? You don't know Scag like we do. When you first meet him, he's like Mr Concerned. Then he changes. He's a bad enemy, kid. There's only one thing he cares about – Carla.

NICKY   Yeah, Carla.

Now **Carla** *is spotlighted, back centre stage.*

CARLA   *fondly* Just call them, Nick. They'll be worried about you. Do it for me.

NICKY I tried to call them. Just once. But, when it came to it, I couldn't say anything.

MR MORRISON *spotlight, stage right. He looks a changed figure, haggard and worried.* Hullo? Hullo? Is that you, Nicky? Listen, if it's you, just tell us – your mother's going mad with worry. We just want to know you're all right. Please, old boy. Hullo? . . . Hullo?

Spotlight dies on him.

NICKY It was like I was trapped. Something bad was on the way. *A spotlight picks up **Scag** standing in the open doorway to his bedroom, staring fixedly at **Nicky**.* But I didn't know how to escape, break out of it.

*Lights up, revealing **Pete** and **Julie** in the kitchen, excitedly reading a newspaper on the kitchen table. **Scag** is still standing in the doorway to the bedroom. **Nicky** slowly approaches them.*

JULIE *seeing **Nicky*** Seems like you're famous, kid.

PETE *reading* 'Concern grows for missing boy. The parents of missing thirteen year-old Nicholas Morrison last night put out an emotional appeal for his return. "We don't know if he's on the run or whether someone's holding him against his will," said Gordon Morrison, a well-known figure in the City of London, announcing a £1000 reward for details of Nicky's whereabouts . . .' Then they give the number of your local nick.

NICKY *stunned* Reward?

JULIE There's a picture and all. You look almost human.

PETE Someone on the street will recognize him, no problem.

JULIE Just what we don't need – a kidnapping rap.

NICKY Forget it – I'd tell them I came here of my own free will.

*Carla comes out of her bedroom, pushes past **Scag** and looks at the paper.*

CARLA Oh no.

NICKY I'll get my stuff – I'm outta here.

PETE Good idea.

CARLA No! *Realizing that her feelings have given her away and that she has reacted too strongly.* I mean, no . . . hurry. Eh, Scag?

19

JULIE   Oh, come on. This guy always was trouble. He's going to drag us down with him.

SCAG   We'll work something out.

NICKY   I'd prefer to go.

SCAG   *coldly*   I wasn't thinking of you. It's the rest of us who have to survive when you're back with Mummy and Daddy.

CARLA   Scag –

SCAG   *to **Nicky***   You can stay until tomorrow. I need you for one more job tonight.   *Nicky looks uncertain.*   Understand, Nick?   *Nicky nods.*   Wait for me in your room. I need to make a call.

*As **Nicky** goes to his room, **Scag** mutters something to **Pete** and **Julie**. **Carla** tries to listen, but **Scag** turns on her.*

SCAG   You leave this to me. One word out of you and –

CARLA   He trusted us, Scag. Let me talk to –   ***Scag** grabs her roughly and pushes her against the wall. She falls to the floor.*

SCAG   I warned you about your little toy boy and I'm warning you again. Stay out of this until it's over, right?   *As **Carla** painfully picks herself up and goes to her bedroom, **Scag** turns to the others.*   Trust! She never learns.   *He leaves through the front door.*

***Julie** and **Pete** sit down and watch the TV. Behind their backs, **Carla** creeps past them to **Nicky's** room. **Nicky** is putting a few things into a shoulder bag. He sees a bruise on her face.*

NICKY   What happened?

CARLA   *putting a finger to her lips*   Nothing. Don't worry.

NICKY   That –

CARLA   Listen. He's turning you in for money. That's what he's setting up now.

NICKY   What? But the police are after him. He can't just wander in –

CARLA   Not him. He'll use his fence in Wandsworth – the guy who gets rid of the cars for him.

NICKY   So now I'm like stolen goods.

CARLA   *taking Nicky's bag*   Just act normal. Leave your gear here – when you're gone I'll leave it behind the dustbins for you to collect later.

NICKY   Carla . . . come with me.

CARLA   *smiling*   I can't. I can't leave him.

NICKY   *caught between desperation and embarrassment*   But . . . the way he treats you. You and me, we . . . Carla –

Carla silences him by placing a finger on his lips. She kisses him on the lips – a tender, light, yet not entirely pure, kiss.

CARLA   One day you'll understand.

NICKY   I'm not a kid, Carla –

But Carla leaves and hurries back to her room.

Lights down – it's night. Scag comes to Nicky's room. They both leave the squat by the front door. After a few moments, Carla appears at the door of her room. She looks at the front door.

CARLA   Good luck, homebird.

Scag and Nicky, on the street at night, enter front stage left. Scag seems more relaxed than usual. They stop, front stage right and Scag offers Nicky a cigarette which he refuses.

NICKY   What are we doing, Scag?

SCAG   *sitting down on the ground*   Waiting.

NICKY   I thought it was a car job.

SCAG   Nope. Not a car job.

They pause.

NICKY   Funny name, Scag. How d'you get it?

For a moment Scag looks angry, then he relaxes – he can afford to since Nicky will soon be history.

SCAG   That's what they called me at school.

NICKY   What's your real name then?   *Scag looks away.*   I won't tell anyone.

SCAG   No. You won't. It was Arlo.

NICKY   Arlo? What's that – a nickname?

SCAG   Hippy name. My parents were really into that lame hippy stuff.

NICKY   My mum's like that – always singing these old songs when she's in the kitchen. My sister Beth's always telling her – *He sees that Scag isn't listening.*   Yeah, well anyway . . .

SCAG   My parents are dead.

NICKY   Oh, I'm sorry – I didn't know.

SCAG   Not dead dead, but dead there.   *He points to his head.*   Dead there.   *He points to his heart. In the distance, a car horn sounds once.*   Dead.

The car horn sounds again.

SCAG   *still preoccupied by the conversation*   Let's go.   *He stands up, waving to his contact, offstage right. While he's distracted, **Nicky** darts off, backstage right.*   You little – ***Scag** sets off in pursuit.*

***Nicky**, on the run, enters front stage left. He shins up some of back scenery, so that he's high above the street. In the shadows, **Scag** enters, stage left, breathing heavily. He looks up and down the street, then runs off, stage right.*

NICKY   See you . . . Arlo.

ACT THREE

*Open stage. A small table with two chairs is backstage right. Backstage left, an **Old Woman** dressed eccentrically in rags, a beggarwoman, is singing 'You are my sunshine', shaking a couple of coins in a plastic cup. While **Nicky** speaks, this is quiet background noise. **Nicky** enters backstage left, carrying the plastic bag containing his things. He looks shattered.*

NICKY   *to the audience*   Eight o'clock in the morning. I'm under Waterloo Bridge. I may have had my face in the papers, but people hurry by me on their way to work as if I'm not there. It's like Invasion of the Zombie Commuters.   *Wearily, he sits down stage left, a few yards from the **Old Woman**.*

OLD WOMAN   *more loudly*   You are my sunshine, my only sunshine.   *She sees **Nicky** slumped wearily.*   You make me happy –

NICKY   I'm hungry.

OLD WOMAN   *to **Nicky**, interrupting her song*   'Ere, son, this is my patch – when skies are blue.   *Nicky ignores her.*   'Ere!

NICKY   *looking up*   Sorry?

OLD WOMAN   Go and doss somewhere else. I was here first.

22

NICKY *too tired to move* Easy, tiger.

Old Woman approaches him and gives him the plastic cup.

OLD WOMAN Make yourself useful then. **Nicky** *doesn't understand* Shake the bloomin' thing! You are my sunshine, my only sunshine. **Nicky** *shakes the plastic cup in time. A woman commuter enters front stage right. She's about to walk past them when she hesitates and puts a coin in the cup. Seconds later a male commuter does the same.* **The Old Woman**, *still singing, winks at him.*

NICKY *to the audience* A great team is born.

The real music for 'You are my sunshine' wells up to accompany the **Old Woman** *– the music continues, she stops singing, looks in the cup, says something to* **Nicky**. *They both shuffle off to the table, stage right. The* **Old Woman** *collects two cups of tea from offstage. The music fades.*

OLD WOMAN *checking her money* Seven pounds eighty. We did all right.

NICKY Yeah. Did you ever think of singing another song?

OLD WOMAN *shocked* They like that one. I tried another one once but it wasn't the same. *Sings* Pack . . . up . . . your . . . troubles in an old kit bag and –

NICKY *quickly* D'you live round here?

OLD WOMAN Who wants to know?

NICKY Me.

OLD WOMAN *still suspicious* Sunningdale. That's where I live. Big house. Lovely beams. Painted all over in a sort of peach. Catches the sunlight in the early morning. Butler. Croquet lawn. Couple of maids.

NICKY *uncertainly* Nice.

OLD WOMAN Very nice. Mind you, I earnt it. I used to drive an ambulance in the war. Saved, oh, hundreds of lives. They were so grateful that Sir Winston Churchill gave us this big house. Of course, that was before my husband was killed leading the Dambusters operation.

NICKY Oh no.

OLD WOMAN He had medals like you wouldn't believe.

NICKY Why . . . why aren't you there now?

OLD WOMAN *looking around her to check no one's*

listening The gardener was in league with the Devil. He used to watch me through the french windows as he dug the rose bed. Red eyes. He was a son of Satan. I had to move out. The Devil's everywhere, even in Sunningdale.

NICKY *realizing how crazy the **Old Woman** is* Oh yeah?

OLD WOMAN Have you got fillings – in your teeth?

NICKY Er, no. I'm a real dentist's pet.

OLD WOMAN Good. They use fillings to tune into your brain, you know. That's how Satan works. Through dentistry.

NICKY *anxious to change the subject* What do they call you?

OLD WOMAN *with a paranoic, crazed laugh* Wouldn't you like to know.

NICKY I need somewhere to sleep tonight. Can I stay with you? I'll work – with the plastic cup.

OLD WOMAN It's cold. You could go to a hostel.

NICKY I don't want to do that.

OLD WOMAN Clever lad. *Nicky looks confused.* The Devil runs them hostels.

NICKY Oh yeah, right. Silly me.

*Lights down. It's night time. The table and chairs have gone. Stage left, a **Tramp**, two **Teenage Dossers** of about **Nicky's** age and the **Old Woman** are gathered around a fire. **Nicky** is standing apart, front stage left.*

NICKY *to the audience* Have you ever slept rough? It's cold – the cold's everywhere. In the air you breathe, seeping from the concrete pavement, in the fabric of your clothes, you're chilled to the marrow of your bones. You don't sleep – you stay up as long as possible, hoping the police won't move you on, hoping there won't be a fight between the winos. There's no glamour to living on the street. And that night, it's lucky that I don't sleep.

FIRST HOMELESS TEENAGER *calling out to **Nicky***
We're goin' up Piccadilly. Wanna come? Show you round.

NICKY No, thanks.

SECOND HOMELESS TEENAGER Come on – be a laugh. You'd do well up there.

NICKY I'm not –

FIRST HOMELESS TEENAGER Make more dosh up there than you will with that old crazy.

24

NICKY Not tonight.

*They leave, crossing the stage. As they reach front stage left, a torch shines in their faces. **Mr Morrison**, looking exhausted with worry, appears. He looks at them, and then walks slowly towards the other dossers. **Nicky** ducks behind a bin. **Mr Morrison** doesn't see him and leaves stage right. **Nicky**, stunned, rejoins the group around the fire.*

OLD WOMAN What's up with you? Seen a ghost?

Nicky shakes his head.

NICKY I'm going home.

OLD WOMAN Oh yeah?

NICKY *thinking aloud* But I want to help you. *The **Old Woman** is suspicious.* The thing is, I'm a runaway – the police are looking for me. There's a reward.

OLD WOMAN Fancy.

NICKY And you're going to get it.

OLD WOMAN Eh?

NICKY Don't you see? You phone the police, tell them where I am – then you can collect the reward. It would get you off the streets – maybe you could go back to Sunningdale.

OLD WOMAN *recoiling* Oh, cunning.

NICKY What?

OLD WOMAN Oh sly. The evil one sends children to tempt me now. Silver-tongued infants to buy my soul.

NICKY But the reward. Don't you understand – it's a thousand pounds.

OLD WOMAN Get thee behind me, Satan! *Nicky stands wearily.* Away! Quit my sight.

NICKY Sorry I mentioned it. *He backs away.* But I know someone else who could use the reward.

OLD WOMAN *as **Nicky** leaves* He held my plastic cup. Satan held my plastic cup.

Nicky exits front stage left. Lights down.

*A blue light is flashing, illuminating the back wall of the stage. It's the exterior of the squat, the front door of which we've seen from the inside in the previous Act is now seen from outside. A distant siren can be heard. As **Nicky** appears front stage right, he crouches down to watch. From behind the door can be heard* *the sound of a struggle. A* **policeman** *emerges at the front door, holding* **Pete**. *He takes him off, stage left. A second* **policeman** *emerges with* **Julie**. **Nicky** *sees* **Scag** *at a top window – he wriggles out, climbs upwards and away. Desperately* **Nicky** *watches the window for* **Carla**–

NICKY   Come on, Carla – escape!

– but **Carla** *appears, looking scared but dignified, at the front door. One of the* **policemen** *goes to take her arm, but she shakes him off and walks proudly towards the police van.* **Nicky** *crumples to the floor.*

It's still night, but later. **Nicky** *is now stage right in a telephone kiosk. He dials a number.*

NICKY   It's me . . . Doesn't matter where I am. Just listen, Mum . . . A friend of mine called Carla Johnson was arrested like three hours ago at a squat in Brixton . . . she was arrested because she contacted the police about me . . . Yeah . . . She's innocent. I need to know that she's being released . . . You know about it? . . . Can you trust him, this policeman . . . Promise she'll be released . . . Promise.   *He sags with relief.* . . . What? Address?   *He looks at the address in front of him in the kiosk.*   Yeah, Jeffreys Road, Brixton.   *Exhausted, he slides down to the floor, and lies slumped for several moments as the lights go down.*

MRS MORRISON   Nicky.

As the lights come up, **Nicky** *is still lying by the telephone kiosk.* **Mrs Morrison** *is approaching him.* **Nicky** *looks up.*

NICKY   Easy . . .   *His mother holds him as* **Mr Morrison, Beth** *and the little dog* **Jessie** *appear on stage.*   Easy . . .

MRS MORRISON   *crying*   Oh Nicky, why did you do it?

MR MORRISON   Come on, old boy.   *He lifts* **Nicky** *up.*   In the car.   *Walks slowly stage right.*

BETH   *crying too*   Talk about Happy Ever After . . .

Nicky *looks up from his father's shoulder and addresses the audience.*

NICKY   Er, no. Not quite.   *He walks slowly back to where he addressed the audience at the start of Act One, as* **Mr Morrison, Mrs Morrison, Beth** *and* **Jessie** *leave stage right. By the time he has reached there, the lighting's exactly the same as it was at the start of the play – he's remembering the story in* *the middle of the night, back in bed.*

NICKY   As usual, Beth's cliché of the moment is a bit wide of the mark. Dad moves out. Not with Jo, the perfect secretary who like dumped him soon after I spoiled their candlelit dinner. He lives in this little flat not far from here, where I go and visit him. It's strange. He's more relaxed now – he listens when you talk, as if he's discovered that you don't have to be a total dictator to be taken seriously. Mum's changed too. She's started going out with some old divorced guy with grey teeth and a really patronising manner. *Imitating him*   Hi-ya, Nicholas. I'm like, No, Mum, not him – please – but she seems happy, so I guess I am too.

Beth's in love. You don't really want to know the details. Just imagine like the biggest cliché in the history of mankind and double it.

I'm back at my old school down the road. Paul – and Quadir – are still at Holton and have promised to give me regular reports from Hell. I'm like, Gee, thanks, guys.

Yesterday I'm walking Jessie in the park when who should I see but Marlon. *Enters **Marlon** in a spotlight, stage right.*   As usual, I ask if he's spoken to Carla recently.

MARLON   Nope. But we got a note from her yesterday. Seems like she's holed up with her lover boy somewhere up north.

NICKY   *disconsolately*   Good old Scag.

MARLON   *about to leave*   Yeah, Mr Teenage Hero. *He's just about to walk away when he remembers something*   Oh. She asked me to give you this. *He hands **Nicky** a note, winks, then leaves stage left.* **Nicky** *opens the envelope and begins to read the letter.*

CARLA   *lit up by a spotlight at the back of centre stage*   Hey, Nick. I wanted to thank you for what you did for me after the bust. You're a true friend. I hope it all worked out for you at home. Things are hot right now for Scag but, believe me, I'll keep in touch with you. Give little Jessie a kiss from me. And one for yourself of course. Grow quickly, homebird. I'll be waiting. All my love, Carla.

NICKY   *getting to his feet, with double-clenched fist gesture of triumph*   Yessss!

STAGING THE PLAY

Before you make any decisions about the staging of the play, look carefully at the acting space available. Your school may have a **proscenium stage** and some rostrums or blocks, so that you can use different levels to indicate different locations. Don't be afraid to experiment with these levels. Explore the ways in which placing actors higher or lower than each other can highlight the dramatic intent in each scene. What, for example, would be the effect in the scene with Pringle to place him on a higher level then the others?

The play requires a number of different settings, so a simple and flexible set will allow the production to flow smoothly with the minimum of interruptions. Try and create the different locations – home, boarding school, street, squat – by using one or two items of furniture which can be moved easily or covered swiftly, in order to avoid holding up the action.

To highlight the contrast between Nicky's comfortable home and the squalor of the squat, you could experiment with designing a reversible flat (a painted wooden frame) with a door and window. One side would be the Morrisons' kitchen – clean and bright with gingham curtains, etc; while the other side could represent the graffiti-covered walls of the squat.

Depending on your resources and your ideas about staging, it might be an idea to have a length of painted flat at the rear of the stage. This could be part chain link, part brick, part fence. By focusing on each area in turn, it could be used as the backdrop to various exterior settings, such as the scene in the park with Marlon, the car theft, begging in Waterloo Station, and so on.

Of course, the large cast is a valuable resource and the actors should be prepared to do more than just play their one part. They could be commuters rushing around outside Waterloo station; the huddled shapes of homeless people that come into view as Nicky's father searches; and a crowd of curious onlookers witnessing the arrest at the squat.

Reversible flat

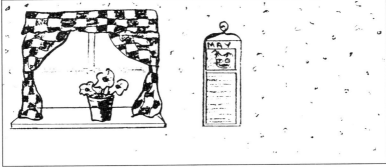

The Morrisons' kitchen

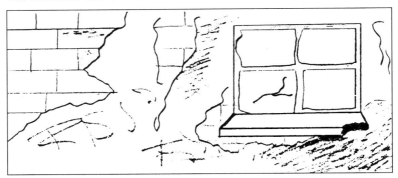

The kitchen of the squat

Set for a proscenium-style stage

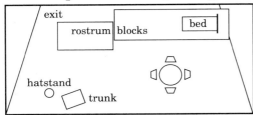

Staging possibilities

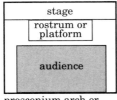

proscenium arch or
platform stage

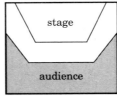

thrust stage

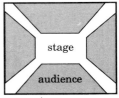

arena stage

There are several occasions in the play when Nicky talks directly to the audience. Choose a specific downstage area for Nicky that is outside the main acting area. Define this space with a spotlight, and place a hatstand and/or trunk in this space for his clothes. He can get changed as he talks to the audience.

Other staging arrangements are possible – a production in the round, for example, or using a thrust stage. Whatever choice you make will have implications for your use of furniture and props, your exits and entrances, and for the acting style. Look at the diagrams and discuss the options open to you.

Costume

Make a list of the costumes you will need. Nicky will need several different ones to show the transitions he goes through. He could start off wearing a black school blazer, then change into a new smart blazer and tie, then into jeans and a T-shirt. In the final scene it is important to make these look as grubby as possible. Maybe he'll need an all-purpose blanket for sleeping and begging in. Remember that at the end of the play there is very little time to make the transformation from street urchin to young teenager back at home, so the costumes must be simple.

Lighting

Lighting should be used subtly to create the play's atmosphere, and should also establish the separate areas of the set. Think how you would create the effect of a flashing police light, or the differences between dawn and dusk. Could you design lighting to suggest dawn, conveying a cold, bleak effect? Experiment with actual lights on stage, for example a bare bulb over the kitchen table in the squat, Nicky's father searching a semi-dark stage with a torch.

Properties

Go through the script and make a list of essential props. Think about props that can set the scene effectively, especially if you are not creating very detailed sets. You will probably only have one table, but with a few props it could be used in several scenes. Mrs Morrison's kitchen table could have a pretty, gingham cloth – when removed, the bare table could be the one in the squat. Similarly, an ornate candlestick and a crisp white tablecloth, quickly set on the table, would 'create' the restaurant atmosphere for the scene between Nicky's father and Jo.

Sound Effects

Sound and music will heighten the atmosphere tremendously. Think about the background noise that you will need, and how you will use it. Radio and TV sounds might be appropriate for home; voices and shouts at the boys school; music at the squat, perhaps muffled as if coming from a neighbouring house; traffic sounds at Waterloo, and so on.

Consider the way that music can emphasise the themes of the play. Make a list of contemporary bands that have written songs about home or homelessness. Here are a few examples: Pet Shop Boys, 'Theatre'; Phil Collins, 'Another Day In Paradise'; Madness, 'Our House'; Arrested Development, 'Mr Wendell'. Try and get hold of the words and music of these songs and see if they could be included in your production.

WORK ON AND AROUND THE SCRIPT

CHARACTER SKETCHES

In the novel of *Homebird*, Terence Blacker has written detailed outlines of certain characters. Here are a couple of examples:

WHO'S WHO AT HOLTON COLLEGE: Pringle.
NAME: Pringle.
CHRISTIAN NAME: None.
AGE: Physical – 17; Mental – 5.
LOOKS: Not pretty. Short red hair. A major zit attack covering his face, neck and shoulders.
LIKES: Causing pain, terror and despair to those smaller than himself.
DISLIKES: More or less everybody but especially Quadir.
FAVOURITE EXPRESSIONS: 'What you looking at, squirt?' 'What you mean nothing, squirt? Calling me nothing, are you?' 'I'm going to knock your teeth so far down your throat you'll need to put a toothbrush up your bum to clean them' etc etc.
STRONG POINT: His right fist and a small, hard point of bone in the centre of his forehead that nature gave him for nutting people.
WEAK POINT: A tendency to lose his temper, followed quickly by a deep need to kill or main.
CAREER PROSPECTS: Will make an excellent psychopathic maniac.

WHO'S WHO IN THE MORRISON FAMILY: My Mum.
NAME: Mary Jean Morrison
AGE: Forty last year (and what a crisis that was).
LOOKS: Nice. Dark hair (bit untidy). Quite slim.
Motherish. Not bad for her age.
LIKES: Flowers, family occasions like Christmas, utterly
gross and embarrassing hits from the sixties.
DISLIKES: Cooking, tidying up, rows, my dad (joke).
HOBBIES: Gardening, finding new things to worry
about.
FAVOURITE EXPRESSIONS: 'Just look at this room!', 'And
what about your homework?', 'Why don't you read a
decent book for a change!', 'If you think I'm clearing
these dishes away, you've got another think coming!',
'Your teeth are GREEN!', 'And WHO do you think is
going to clean this?' plus several other things that like
end in a '!'or a '?'
STRONG POINT: She sticks up for her son in arguments
with Dad or my sister Beth.
WEAK POINT: Being a total stress case.

Choose a couple of other characters from the play and, using
the same format, write similar outlines for them. Compare
your work with the rest of the class. You won't necessarily
have the same points of view about the characters – compare
your outlines, and discuss the differences and similarities.

This activity could be expanded by writing similar outlines
of yourself, your own family and friends.

REVIEWS

The novel of *Homebird* has also been published in the United
States. When it first came out there, it was reviewed in
American newspapers and magazines. Read the two reviews
below.

Nicky Morrison lives in London with his parents and sister
until his father decides a boarding school might help him
improve his grades. At Holton, he defends a misfit classmate
and is beaten up by the school bully. Running away, Nicky
goes to his father's office to enlist his help, but is devastated

when he sees that his father has a romantic relationship with his secretary. Now, Nicky is also running from his family and its problems, and he winds up living in an abandoned building with five other teenagers, who support themselves through various illegal activities. Nicky tolerates the abject squalor and perfidy of his housemates because it seems easier than dealing with his father's betrayal. Weak from hunger and sought by the police for a robbery, he witnesses the arrest of his only friend in the house, and finally tells his family where he is. Blacker does not deliver a happily-ever-after ending, but he does show people who have learned from their mistakes and from each other. This short book tells a taut, complex story with a believable protagonist and some fascinating supporting characters.

Booklist

This novel will fascinate anyone who has ever imagined what it would be like to slip "from the cozy, secure world of right and wrong and fridges and table manners and TV every night into the cold outside where the only success is to survive another day". Nicky, 13, runs away from his British boarding school after his altruistic defense of a fellow student earns him a brutal beating. Nicky's plans to return home are stymied, however, when he discovers his father is having an affair. Angry and virtually penniless, the boy hooks up with the teenaged residents of a Brixton "squat", and drifts into a life of crime. Authentically adolescent, Nicky's voice manages to achieve just the right balance between sarcasm and sensitivity; all that is trite and cloying is avoided – or as Nicky says "Now whoa there – check that major cliché attack." The wisecracking first-person narrative, peppered with thumbnail sketches of various characters and snatches of imagined screenplay dialogue, along with a bouncy MTV-like style of quick cutting from one scene to the next, makes this an ideal book for reluctant readers.

Publishers Weekly

- Do you agree with these reviews? Is what they say about the story correct? How can you tell that the reviews were written by Americans? What particular problems do you think American readers would encounter in the story?

- Write your own review of the play.

THE FAMILY

1 Tableaux

A tableau is a representation of a scene by a person or group posed silently and motionlessly. Create a series of tableaux of Nicky's family as if they are taken from a photo album showing the changing relationships in the family over the years. Set up three or four tableaux that bring us up to the point when we first meet Nicky.

2 Nicky's future

Organisation: Work with a partner, imagining that you are Nicky's parents. Read the first scene again, and decide what kind of people you are.

Situation: Improvise a scene in which you discuss Nicky's progress at school. Who is the first to suggest boarding school? Whose idea is the present of a dog? Try to let your conversation reveal your characters' concerns, e.g. Nicky's father's preoccupation with success and hard work. Who decides how to break the news to Nicky about his new school?

First line (Mr Morrison): **What are we going to do about that boy?**

Extension: Imagine *you* are being sent to boarding school. You are allowed to bring a small bag of personal belongings with you, in addition to your clothes. What will you decide to pack? In the play Quadir's most precious possession is his copy of the Koran. Do you have anything which means as much to you?

3 Beth's view

Organisation: Work with a partner. Imagine that one of you is Beth, and the other is a new friend.

Situation: Beth is discussing her family and, in particular, her younger brother Nicky, with her friend.

First line: (Beth): **Nicky really gets on my nerves sometimes.**

Extension: Make a list of words which describe Nicky, another list for Beth and one for each of their parents.

4 Looking for Nicky

Organisation: Work in a group of three. Imagine that one of you is the Headmaster of Holton, and the others are Nicky's friends, Paul and Quadir.

Situation: Nicky's disappearance has been discovered. How will you explain it to the Headmaster? Will you tell him what you know or will you try to put him off the scent? If you tell the Headmaster about Pringle, will he believe you? What proof can you give him?

First Line (Headmaster): **This is a very serious situation.**

Extension: Read the letter that Nicky writes to his parents from school, and then write the letter that Nicky might really have wanted to send them, describing his problems at school.

5 Bullying

Organisation: Work in a large group, or even with the whole class. Each of you should play a member of the Holton school staff, a school governor or a parent. Your teacher might also take on a role, perhaps being the Headteacher.

Situation: The staff at Holton are very disturbed about evidence of bullying which has come to light. A special meeting is called to discuss the problem with concerned parents and governors.

First line (Headmaster): **I'm sure that between us we can solve this problem**.

Extension: Write a report that might appear in the local paper about the situation at Holton School.

BULLIES IN LITERATURE

Tom Brown's Schooldays by Thomas Hughes was published in 1857. Like Nicky, Tom is at boarding school. He too has a problem with the school bully, but solves it in a different way.

Well, one evening, in forbidden hours, Tom and East were in the Hall. They occupied the seats before the fire nearest the door, while Diggs sprawled as usual before the further fire. He was busy with a copy of verses, and East and Tom were chatting together in whispers by the light of the fire, and splicing a favourite old fives'-bat which had sprung. Presently a step came down the bottom passage; they listened a moment, assured themselves that it wasn't a praepostor, and then went on with their work, and the door swung open, and in walked Flashman. He didn't see Diggs, and thought it a good chance to keep his hand in; and as the boys didn't move for him, struck one of them, to make them get out of his way.

'What's that for?' growled the assaulted one.

'Because I choose. You've no business here - go to your study.'

'You can't send us.'

'Can't I? Then I'll thrash you if you stay,' said Flashman savagely.

'I say, you two,' said Diggs from the end of the Hall, rousing up and resting himself on his elbow, 'you'll never get rid of that fellow till you lick him. Go in at him, both of you - I'll see fair play.'

Flashman was taken aback, and retreated two steps. East looked at Tom. 'Shall we try?' said he. 'Yes,' said Tom desperately. So the two advanced on Flashman with clenched fists and beating hearts. They were about up to his shoulder, but tough boys of their age and in perfect training, while he, though strong and big, was in poor condition from his monstrous habits of stuffing and want of exercise. Coward as he was, however, Flashman couldn't swallow such an insult as this; besides, he was confident of having easy work, and so faced the boys, saying, 'You impudent young blackguards!' - Before he could finish his abuse they rushed in on him, and began pummelling at all of him which they could reach. He hit out wildly and savagely, but the full force of his blows didn't tell, they were too near him. It was long odds tho' in point of strength, and in another minute Tom went spinning backwards over a form, and Flashman turned to demolish East with a savage grin. But now Diggs jumped

Began pummelling at all of him which they could reach

down from the table on which he had seated himself. 'Stop there,' shouted he, 'the round's over - half-minute time allowed.' 'What the - is it to you?' faltered Flashman, who began to lose heart.

'I'm going to see fair, I tell you,' said Diggs with a grin, and snapping his great red fingers; ''tain't fair for you to be fighting one of them at a time. Are you ready, Brown? Time's up.' The small boys rushed in again. Closing they saw their best chance and Flashman was wilder and more flurried than ever: he caught East by the throat and tried to force him back on the iron-bound table; Tom grasped his waist, and remembering the old throw he had learned in the Vale from Harry Winburn, crooked his leg inside Flashman's, and threw his whole weight forward. The three tottered for a moment, and then over they went on to the floor, Flashman striking his head against a form in the fall.

The two youngsters sprang to their legs, but he lay there still. They began to be frightened. Tom stooped down, and then cried out, scared out of his wits, 'He's bleeding awfully; come here, East, Diggs - he's dying!'

'Not he,' said Diggs, getting leisurely off the table; 'it's all sham, he's only afraid to fight it out.'

East was as frightened as Tom. Digg's lifted Flashman's head,and he groaned.

'What's the matter?' shouted Diggs.

'My skull's fractured,' sobbed Flashman.

'Oh, let me run for the housekeeper,' cried Tom. 'What shall we do?'

'Fiddlesticks! it's nothing but the skin broken,' said the relentless Diggs, feeling his head. 'Cold water and a bit of rag's all he'll want.'

'Let me go,' said Flashman, surlily, sitting up; 'I don't want your help.'

'We're really very sorry,' began East.

'Hang your sorrow,' answered Flashman, holding his handkerchief to the place; 'you shall pay for this, I can tell you, both of you.' And he walked out of the Hall.

'He can't be very bad,' said Tom with a deep sigh, much relieved to see his enemy march so well.

'Not he,' said Diggs, 'and you'll see you won't be troubled with him any more. But, I say, your head's broken too - your collar is covered with blood.'

'Is it though?' said Tom, putting up his hand, 'I didn't know it.'

'Well, mop it up, or you'll have your jacket spoilt. And you have got a nasty eye, Scud; you'd better go and bathe it well in cold water.'

'Cheap enough too, if we've done with our old friend Flashey,' said East, as they made off upstairs to bathe their wounds.

Discussion

1. Contrast Nicky's behaviour with that of Tom Brown's. Do you think Flashman is a worse bully than Pringle; if so, in what way? What would Pringle have done if Nicky and Paul had fought him?
   What do you think life was like for Tom Brown after his fight? Do you think Flashman's behaviour changed for better or for worse?

2. Does 'Taking the law into your own hands' work? Can you think of some recent examples in the news when people have done this? Why have they done this, and what is usually the end result?

Staging the fight

1. Read the extract carefully. In groups of four, try to stage this scene. Pay particular attention to the fight sequence. Plan it thoroughly so that it looks realistic without anyone being in danger of injury.
2. Write down your fight sequence in detail. Try to imagine it being filmed for television. Write a screenplay, i.e. a sequence of camera moves, as if you were directing the fight for TV. A clearer way of writing the shots that you want may be in the form of diagrams or stick figures.
3. Discuss your screenplay with the others in the group. What changes – if any – do you need to make to your original fight to make it work on film rather than on the stage.

ON THE RUN

Looking for Nicky

1 Explanations

Organisation: Work with a partner, imagining that one of you
is Nicky and the other is Mr Morrison.

Situation: Mr Morrison thinks he sees his son outside the
restaurant where he has taken Jo. He catches up with Nicky
and attempts an explanation.

First line (Mr Morrison): **Nicky, wait! What are you doing
here?**

2 Police Report

Organisation: Work in groups of three or four. Two of you
should play Mr and Mrs Morrison, one should be a police
officer and, if there are four of you, include Beth.

Situation: Nicky's family have reported his disappearance to
the authorities. A police officer has come to see the family to
try and find out why he's run away – who saw him last, what
his state of mind was, etc. How much information does
Nicky's father give?

First line (Police officer): **It will help us to find Nicholas if
you give us as much information as possible.**

3 Suspicions

Organisation: Work in the same groups without the police
officer.

Situation: The police officer has left. Carry on the scene
exploring what has or has not been revealed by Mr Morrison.

First Line (Mrs Morrison): **What is it? I felt you were
holding something back.**

IN THE SQUAT

1 Dreams of the future

In Act II, Nicky day-dreams about what might happen if he went home and talked to his father 'man to man'. Later, he tells Carla about his idealized picture of his family. Working with a small group, imagine that Nicky has a dream during his first night at the squat about going home. Create the dream, in which everything goes just the way Nicky would like and his family welcomes him with open arms. Remember that everything in a dream is exaggerated and unrealistic, and movement and sound may be repeated and distorted.

2 Squatters' rights

Some of the squat members don't want Nicky to stay; others do. In groups of four, improvise a scene in which they discuss the problem. What does your conversation reveal about the squat? Does everyone have 'equal say'?

3 Carla and Scag

Scag is not happy about Carla's friendship with Nicky. In pairs, improvise a scene in which Julie asks Carla why she stays with Scag. Alternatively, create a scene where Nicky questions Pete about Carla and Scag's relationship.

Extensions: Write a longer letter from Carla to Nicky about her relationship with Scag. Write a letter from Nicky's mother to him explaining why she and his father have separated.

4 The Theft

In the play, Nicky does not question the car theft, yet earlier he is quick to defend the issue of right and wrong at the school. Improvise a scene between him and Scag in which Scag tells him what they are going to do. How would Scag persuade him to help?

5 Discussion

Compare Scag and Pringle. In what ways are they similar and in what ways different? Scag could be described as an anti-hero: a central character who lacks the traditional heroic virtues but retains some charisma. Can you come up with a list of anti-heroes from history, real-life, film or TV?

FAGIN'S DEN

Read the following extract from *Oliver Twist* by Charles
Dickens. Discuss the characters and how they came to be in
this situation. Why does Nancy get so upset? What could she
do to help Oliver?

'Keep back the dog, Bill!' cried Nancy, springing before the door,
and closing it, as the Jew [Fagin] and his two pupils darted out in
pursuit. 'Keep back the dog; he'll tear the boy to pieces.'
Serve him right!' cried Sikes, struggling to disengage himself
from the girl's grasp. 'Stand off from me, or I'll split your skull
against the wall.'
I don't care for that, Bill, I don't care for that,' screamed the girl,
struggling violently with the man: 'the child shan't be torn apart
by the dog, unless you kill me first.'
'Shan't he!' said Sikes, setting his teeth fiercely. 'I'll soon do that,
if you don't keep off.'
The housebreaker flung the girl from him to the farther end of
the room, just as the Jew and the two boys returned, dragging
Oliver among them.
'What's the matter here!' said the Jew, looking round.
'The girl's gone mad, I think,' replied Sikes, savagely.
'No, she hasn't,' said Nancy, pale and breathless from the scuffle;
'no, she hasn't, Fagin; don't think it.'
'Then keep quiet, will you?' said the Jew, with a threatening look.
'No, I won't do that, neither,' replied Nancy, speaking very loud.
'Come! What do you think of that?'
Mr Fagin was sufficiently well acquainted with the manners and
customs of that particular species of humanity to which Nancy
belonged, to feel tolerably certain that it would be rather unsafe
to prolong any conversation with her, at present. With the view
of diverting the attention of the company, he turned to Oliver.
'So you wanted to get away, my dear, did you?' said the Jew,
taking up a jagged and knotted club which lay in a corner of the
fireplace; 'eh?'
Oliver made no reply. But he watched the Jew's motions, and
breathed quickly.
'Wanted to get assistance; called for the police; did you?'
sneered the Jew, catching the boy by the arm. 'We'll cure you of
that, my young master.'
The Jew inflicted a smart blow on Oliver's shoulders with the
club; and was raising it for a second, when the girl, rushing
forward, wrested it from his hand. She flung it into the fire, with

a force that brought some of the glowing coals whirling out
into the room.

'I won't stand by and see it done, Fagin,' cried the girl.

'You've got the boy, and what more would you have? – Let him
be – let him be – or I shall put that mark on some of you, that
will bring me to the gallows before my time.'

The girl stamped her foot violently on the floor as she vented
this threat; and with her lips compressed, and her hands
clenched, looked alternately at the Jew and the other robber:
her face quite colourless from the passion of rage into which she
had gradually worked herself.

- The characters in this extract bear a remarkable
  resemblance to the characters in *Homebird*. Make a list of
  differences and similarities between Nancy and Carla, Bill
  Sikes and Scag, and Oliver and Nicky. Then share your
  ideas with the rest of the class.

- Imagine the scene which comes directly before this one.
  Make notes on what could have happened to lead to this
  situation. Then, either write the scene, as it might appear
  in the novel, or share your ideas with a small group and act
  it out for the rest of the class.

FROM NOVEL TO PLAY

In the novel of *Homebird*, Terence Blacker provides more
detail of life on the streets.

Read the following extract. Why do you think the writer did
not include this scene in the play? Do we learn anything new
about Nicky from this extract? Would it be possible to
dramatise this scene successfully?

The car pulls up outside this big off-licence, selling all kinds of
drink. Casually, John turns round to me and says, 'We're looking
for a place on Half Moon Lane. Ask the geezer in there
directions, will you, Nick?' He nods to the drinks shop where a
middle-aged Asian man is standing behind the till.

'And, if he doesn't know,' adds Pete, 'ask him which road we
should take for Piccadilly. Just keep him talking, right?'

'We'll be doing a bit of shopping,' John says. 'If we come in,
don't talk to us.'

So I get out and go into the store. The Asian has that tired look
of someone who spends his whole life working.

'You have to be eighteen to buy alcohol,' he goes as I approach
the till.

I say, 'I'm looking for Half Moon Lane. You couldn't point me in
the right direction, could you?'

There's something entirely innocent about my voice and
manner. Even after nearly ten days on the run, I seem to be a
person to be trusted.

'Half Moon Lane,' he goes. 'Now that's Streatham way, I think.'
From under the till, he takes out this street directory and starts
thumbing through the pages.

'Ah yes,' he mutters. 'It's not close. It's a bit complicated. Are
your parents taking you?'

'Yes,' I go. 'My dad.'

We're both looking at the map when John and Pete wander in. I
glance up, but, remembering my instructions, I return to the
map.

'Left at that main road?' I ask.

There's a clinking of bottles behind us and, out of the corner of my eye, I see that John and Pete are filling two shopping baskets full of spirits and wine. Suddenly I know what's going to happen but I'm powerless to act.

As if sensing my change of mood, the shopkeeper glances up - just as the boys pull open the door and, holding the baskets to their chests, run for it.

'Hey!' With surprising speed, the Asian leaps from behind the till and out of the door but Pete must have left the car engine running because, with a squeal of tyres, they're off and away. Thanks, guys.

I'm still in shock when the shopkeeper returns. He closes the door behind him and locks it.

'Nice friends you've got,'he says, breathing heavily.

'Me?' My mouth is so dry I can hardly speak. 'I never – I never met them.'

'You can tell that to the police,' goes the man, walking quickly to the phone while keeping a wary eye on me.

'Don't try anything, all right.' He glances to his left where, for the first time, I see a security camera.

'You're on film anyway.'

Like I was someone out of a dream, I take a deep breath and grab a bottle behind me, bringing it down with full force on the side of the till. Trying to keep the panic out of my voice, I scream, 'Open the door or I –' Desperately, I try to think what Scag would say '– Or I bloody re-arrange your face!'

The man's eyes widen but he says, 'Don't make it worse than it is or –'

'Do it!' I scream, jabbing in his direction with the broken bottle-top.

'You're bloody little fool,' he says but, seeing the look in my eyes, he backs towards the door and unlocks it.

'Open it for me.'

With a shrug, the Asian holds the door open. 'Leave the broken bottle and we'll forget all –'

But, throwing the bottle to the ground, I hurl myself through the door and sprint down the High Street, my eyes stinging with tears. I dart down one side road, then another, before I reach a back road where there's a rubbish tip. Through the gloom, I look back down the street. All's quiet now, not even the distant siren of a police car.

I bury my face in my hands and sob in the darkness.

Read and discuss the extract below, from *Oliver Twist*.
What is going on? Why are the gang using Oliver? How
does Oliver feel?

After walking about a quarter of a mile, they stopped before a
detached house surrounded by a wall: to the top of which, Toby
Crackit, scarcely pausing to take breath, climbed in a twinkling.
'The boy next,' said Toby. 'Hoist him up; I'll catch him under the
arms'; and in three or four seconds he and Toby were lying on
the grass on the other side. Sikes followed directly. And they
stole cautiously towards the house.

And now, for the first time, Oliver, well-nigh mad with grief and
terror, saw that housebreaking and robbery, if not murder, were
the objects of the expedition. He clasped his hands together,
and involuntarily uttered a subdued exclamation of horror. A
mist came before his eyes; the cold sweat stood upon his ashy
face; his limbs failed him; and he sank upon his knees.

'Get up!' murmured Sikes, trembling with rage, and drawing the
pistol from his pocket; 'Get up, or I'll strew your brains upon the
grass'.

'Oh! for God's sake let me go!' cried Oliver; 'let me run away
and die in the fields. I will never come near London; never,
never! Oh! pray have mercy on me, and do not make me steal.
For the love of all the bright Angels that rest in Heaven, have
mercy upon me!'

The man to whom this appeal was made swore a dreadful oath,
and had cocked the pistol, when Toby, striking it from his grasp,
placed his hand upon the boy's mouth, and dragged him to the
house.

'Hush!' cried the man; 'it won't answer here. Say another word,
and I'll do your business myself with a crack on the head. That
makes no noise, and is quite as certain, and more genteel. Here,
Bill, wrench the shutter open. He's game enough now, I'll
engage. I've seen older hands of his age took the same way, for
a minute or two, on a cold night.'

Sikes, invoking terrific imprecations upon Fagin's head for
sending Oliver on such an errand, plied the crowbar vigorously,
but with little noise. After some delay, and some assistance from
Toby, the shutter to which he had referred, swung open on its
hinges.

It was a little lattice window, about five feet and a half above the ground, at the back of the house: which belonged to a scullery, or small brewing-place, at the end of the passage. The aperture was so small, that the inmates had probably not thought it worth while to defend it more securely; but it was large enough to admit a boy of Oliver's size, nevertheless. A very brief exercise of Mr Sike's art sufficed to overcome the fastening of the lattice; and it soon stood wide open also.

'Now listen, you young limb,' whispered Sikes, drawing a dark lantern from his pocket, and throwing the glare full on Oliver's face; 'I'm a going to put you through there. Take this light; go softly up the steps straight afore you, and along the little hall, to the street-door; unfasten it, and let us in.'

'There's a bolt at the top, you won't be able to reach,' interposed Toby. 'Stand upon one of the hall chairs. There are three there, Bill, with a jolly large blue unicorn and gold pitchfork on 'em: which is the old lady's arms.'
'Keep quiet, can't you?' replied Sikes, with a threatening look. 'The room-door is open, is it?'
'Wide,' replied Toby, after peeping in to satisfy himself. 'The game of that is, that they always leave it open with a catch, so that the dog, who's got a bed in here, may walk up and down the passage when he feels wakeful. Ha! ha! Barney 'ticed him away tonight. So neat!'

Although Mr Crackit spoke in a scarcely audible whisper, and laughed without noise, Sikes imperiously commanded him to be silent, and to get to work. Toby complied, by first producing his lantern, and placing it on the ground; then by planting himself firmly with his head against the wall beneath the window, and his hands upon his knees, so as to make a step of his back. This was no sooner done, than Sikes, mounting upon him, put Oliver gently through the window with his feet first; and, without leaving hold of his collar, planted him safely on the floor inside.

'Take this lantern,' said Sikes, looking into the room. 'You see the stairs afore you?'
Oliver, more dead than alive, gasped out 'Yes'. Sikes, pointing to the street-door with the pistol-barrel, briefly advised him to take notice that he was within shot all the way; and that if he faltered, he would fall dead that instant.
'It's done in a minute,' said Sikes, in the same low whisper. 'Directly I leave go of you, do your work. Hark!'

'What's that?' whispered the other man.

They listened intently.

'Nothing,' said Sikes, releasing his hold of Oliver. 'Now!'

In the short time he had had to collect his senses, the boy had firmly resolved that, whether he died in the attempt or not, he would make one effort to dart up stairs from the hall, and alarm the family. Filled with this idea, he advanced at once, but stealthily.

'Come back!' suddenly cried Sikes aloud. 'Back! Back!'

Scared by the sudden breaking of the dead stillness of the place, and by a loud cry which followed it, Oliver let his lantern fall, and knew not whether to advance or fly.

- Compare these two extracts. Both Nicky and Oliver are involved in robberies against their will. They are both taken to the scene of the crime by the thieves, without knowing what is going on. However, when they do realize what is happening, Nicky and Oliver react in different ways.

- How does each boy react, and why do you think they react so differently? Which extract is more plausible and why?

- Choose one or two paragraphs from the second extract and rewrite them in modern English.

HISTORICAL BACKGROUND

Abandoned, orphaned or runaway children have always
existed, but concern for these children, and efforts to help
them, have come about only comparatively recently. There
have, however, always been people ready to exploit these
children and force them into crime.

In the sixteenth century these criminals were very well
organised. This extract from a letter of 1588, from Fleetwood
the Recorder to the Lord Treasurer, describes how children
were taught to steal.

A great many [criminals] were found in London,
Westminster, Southwark, and places about the same.
And they got the names of forty-five masterless men and
cut-purses, whose purpose was to rob gentlemen's
chambers and artificers shops, in and about London, and
seven houses of entertainment for such in London. Six
more in Westminster; three more in the suburbs, and two
in Southwark. Among the rest they found out one Wotton,
a gentleman born, and some time a merchant of good
credit, but fallen by time into decay. This man kept an
Alehouse at Smartskey near Billingsgate, and after, for
save this demeanour, put down, he reared up a new trade
of life: and in the same house he procured all the cut-
purses about the city to repair to his house. There was a
school-house set up to learn young boys to cut purses.
Two devices were hung up; one was a pocket, and
another was a purse. The pocket had in it certain
counters, and was hung about with hawks-bells, and over
the top did hang a little sacring bell. The purse had silver
in it: And he that could take out a counter without any
noise was allowed to be a publick *foyster*. And he that
could take a piece of silver out of the purse without noise
of any of the Bells, was adjudged a *judicial nypper*,
according to the terms of their art. A *foyster* was a pick-
pocket, a *nypper* was a pick-purse or cut-purse.'

- How do you think these children came to be in this situation?
- What is the difference between a pick-pocket and a cut-purse?
- In modern English explain how the children were trained.

On Trial

Two young cut-purses have been arrested by the beadle, and brought before the magistrate. Their rich victim is there, together with a small jury. Do you think the young thieves would have anyone to defend them in court? Perhaps a sympathetic clergyman would speak for them. Would they reveal the existence of the 'gang'? Would it help their case to do so? What would be the differences in the way these children would be dealt with compared to nowadays? Find out what the likely punishments might have been. Working with the whole class, act out the trial.

TAKING CARE OF RUNAWAYS

Not everyone was trying to exploit homeless children. In 1552 Christ's Hospital (The Blue Coat Hospital) was opened in London for the care and education of, initially, 380 orphans. The boys were taught Maths, Latin and Greek, and each year ten boys were apprenticed to the Royal Navy. They had to wear a special silver badge when in town in order to avoid being 'pressed' into service in the Navy by the notorious Press Gangs. The girls were taught to read the Bible and to sew.

Although Christ's Hospital saved the lives of many children, it made little overall difference to the nationwide problem of homeless children.

The only remedy the authorities had for dealing with beggars and vagrants was to move them on to the next parish. They were often tied to the back of a cart and whipped through the market-place, children as well as adults.

It became clear that whipping, putting people in stocks and sending them back to their original parishes did nothing to prevent the numbers of homeless children increasing. For a while child beggars were transported to the Colonies to be trained as farmers. The intention was to give children a fresh start in a new environment, and prevent them from embarking on a 'life of idlenesse'. As recently as the 1950s, large numbers of children from British orphanages were shipped overseas to Australia and Canada. Some ended up working in appalling conditions as cheap labour.

The notorious 'Bridewells' were prisons where child felons were sent to serve their sentences alongside adult criminals. No distinction in the severity of punishment was made between children and adults; if the penalty for a particular crime was hanging, children were hanged.

By the eighteenth century the government was taking legal steps to solve the problem of homelessness.

• 1733 - an Act was passed to allow parishes to build workhouses to house the destitute. Under the new Act, Parish Relief, a sort of Unemployment Benefit, could be refused to anyone who did not enter a workhouse.

The notion that homelessness snd poverty were crimes was deeply entrenched in public attitudes. Forcing children into apprenticeships, transportation or sending them to the workhouse were thought to be suitable punishment for these 'crimes'.

• 1824 - The Vagrancy Act was passed making it an offence to beg in a public place.

• 1839 - Section 64 of the Metropolitan Police Act states that people can be taken into custody if they are found between sunset and 8am 'lying or loitering in any highway, yard or other place, and not giving a satisfactory account of themselves'. This law is still in use today.

As the story of Oliver Twist demonstrates, homeless children could have been escaping a cruel employer rather than running away from their families. The only options available to these children in the ninteenth century were crime and begging, and yet the numbers of homeless children continued to swell. One reason for this was the Industrial Revolution which resulted in the break-up of rural communities as people left their families and went to the towns to find work in the new factories.

• 1867 - Dr Barnardo opened his Children's Home with the motto 'No Destitute Child Ever Turned Away'.

• 1869 - The National Children's Home was established which has fed, clothed and trained over 47,000 girls and boys.

• 1875 - The New York Society for the Prevention of Cruelty to Children was formed. The idea was brought to England and the first branch was opened in Liverpool in 1881.

In the 1930s the Depression and high unemployment levels caused the break-up of many families. Children ran away from home or were abandoned.

The following extract examines the problem of homelessness and vagrancy among the young in this century.

Hitching lifts in lorries, sleeping in hedges, begging a crust and a drink here and there, teen-aged boys made their way [to London] expecting to find the streets paved with gold. They were the fodder of the hotel kitchens, a constantly moving and self-renewing source of cheap labour. They were lost in the antheap of the great metropolis which had lured them and used them but had no real need of them, because it, too, had a considerable pool of unemployed. All too often they ended up back in the dole queue, or hung about the automatic machines in the amusement arcades and drifted into petty crime. Others swelled the ranks of the down-and-outs sleeping under a covering of newspapers on the Embankment or in a Salvation Army hostel. Some, terrified by the endless streets of London, headed for the open road beyond and became tramps.

The call of the open road, like the lure of London, worked powerfully on the imagination of youth but led only to disillusion. Rescuing lads from the road was the mission of a number of small voluntary groups, one of which was Waterside House at Willesborough, in Kent. It had started as a rented, tumbledown, eight-roomed house in a Maidstone slum before it moved to a house in 4½ acres where twenty-five lads could be housed at one time. One of its committee helpers explained: "Half the battle of rescuing boys off the road is to accustom them to work again.

During their wanderings they have lost so many things - not only their job, but independence, self-respect, friends, hopes, initiative, and the power to work - and all these things have to be recovered before they are fit to keep a job..."

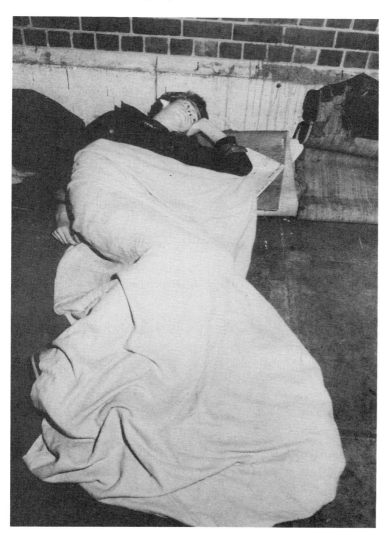

But once a boy had become a tramp it was no easy task to get him back into regular work. Out of 226 young vagrants aged between fourteen and twenty-one who were accepted into Gray House at Bicester only twenty-one remained in the jobs that were found for them. The rest were either dismissed or absconded to return to vagrancy or crime. This noble experiment lasted for only three years and Mr Frank Gray, who launched it, died in the knowledge that it had been a failure. Like Dr Barnardo in the previous century, he had the courage to tackle a seemingly impossible task, and when this twentieth-century effort collapsed, the joint vagrancy committee of the countries of Berkshire, Buckinghamshire and Oxfordshire commented pompously: "So long as legislation, casual wards and indiscriminate private charity enable and encourage youths to take to the road, there will never be a lack of habitual vagrants and criminals."

When the statement was made, in 1935, the workhouse was supposed to be dead, but the attitudes of an institution which had lasted a hundred years were not so easily disposed of. Boy tramps were a particularly scandalous feature of the Depression and the voluntary efforts to rescue them concentrated on those who were physically and mentally fit – the rest were left in the casual wards amidst the other outcasts of society.

From *A Cry From The Streets* by Frank Dawes

- Why do you think Frank Gray's project was a failure?

- Using your library, find out as much as possible about the Depression of the 1930s. What caused families to break up during this period?

HOMELESS IN THE 1990S

What help can homeless youngsters get nowadays?
Centrepoint is one institution helping the homeless today by
running a Shelter. The following passages are taken from
Centrepoint Soho's booklet, *Days to Remember*.

HELPING NEWLY HOMELESS YOUNG PEOPLE

Centrepoint runs an emergency hostel for newly homeless young
people at risk on the streets of London. Many have spent most of
their lives in Care or have been thrown out by their parents. Some
have come to London to look for work; others have run away from
intolerable situations. All of them come to The Shelter because they
have no money, nowhere to stay and no-one else to turn to.

The Shelter aims to give these young people a breathing space.
Staff and volunteers listen, assess with them what has gone wrong
and help them decide what to do next. All will need help getting
money and finding a place to live. Most will also have other needs
from counselling to finding a job, to rebuilding relationships with their
family if this is possible. Many will be referred to other specialist
agencies to help with this.

A Day to Remember ... for Paul (17)
A young person at The Shelter

'When I first came to The Shelter I'd been awake for 40 hours and
walked about 20 miles.

I'd come down from Liverpool with my girlfriend because my dad had
said "Get a job or get out", but we couldn't find jobs at home. We had
£300 and the address of a friend in Tottenham. We'd planned to find
work and then get our own place to live.

But things started to go wrong as soon as we got off the coach.
Someone stole our money so when we arrived in London we were
penniless. We didn't even have the train fare to Tottenham so we
walked from Victoria. When we got to Tottenham we couldn't find my
friend's place. We walked around for hours but no-one seemed to have
heard of it.

In the end we decided we'd better walk back to central London. Someone directed us to Centrepoint in Berwick Street. We were so relieved that they could take us both. They gave us food and shelter and the staff were really understanding.

Without Centrepoint we would have been in dire straits. I'm frightened to think what might have happened to us. I know that London is not the place to be if you've no money and nowhere to go. We might have had to sleep on the streets.

I'm glad I was asked to tell my story. If Centrepoint helped me, it could help other people too.'

Paul

The Hostel

In role, your teacher can work as the houseparent of a new hostel which will provide temporary accommodation for young people who have run away from home. Half the group should take on the roles of volunteer helpers, the other half should play the first batch of arrivals at the hostel.

The houseparent and volunteers plan the layout and amenities that the hostel should have. Individually, the new arrivals decide on a number of biographical details – names, ages, family, etc.

DAY ONE
1. The hostel is ready and the new arrivals are welcomed.
2. In pairs, each arrival is interviewed by a volunteer about their background and the reasons they left home.
3. The arrivals meet and tell each other their backgrounds. The volunteers, meanwhile, make reports on their clients to the houseparent.
4. The residents are given some responsibilty for drawing up the rules for the hostel. These rules can cover the practical aspects of running the household, as well as leisure activities, and personal behaviour inside and outside the hostel.
6. These rules are presented and discussed with the volunteers.
7. The residents are then asked to pause and think about the first day's events. They can either talk or write about their impressions and thoughts about
   a) the good things about their present situation and
   b) the one thing they miss about their home.

ON THE STREETS IN THE 1990s

■ The Old Woman at Waterloo Station

• Create a series of scenes which reveal how the old woman who befriends Nicky might have come to be on the streets. You should think about her childhood, her school life, her marriage. Introduce other characters from her past. In turns, ask each one to tell the rest of the group their opinions about her.

• Imagine you are an experienced psychiatrist. Write a psychiatric report on the old woman, recommending appropriate action or treatment.

■ Look at the photograph above of a policeman speaking to a young homeless person, and write the dialogue to accompany the scene.

■ TRAMPS ON WATERLOO STATION

It is 2 a.m. and I wait for a train out of London.
There is nothing to do but sit and wait
On the cold, darkened platform under clocks.
Newspaper vans unload news of governments,
Or Science and sex. There are men around me
Pretending to be travellers, passing time
Expertly in shadows and corners.
Some sleep with oblique heads on chests
Others embrace warm coffee machines
And stare and wait and ache with silence.
A man talks to himself quietly, facing
A wall and pointing at someone invisible.
As he moves from darkness to sanity he lifts
Up his head and sings an Irish song.
The notes unburden his eyeshut face
And a curved smile links him to a precious
Moment from the păst. A man in rags
Lies in a heap on a bench in a bookshop shadow.
He uncurls himself like a tropical plant and
His face is a dark map of his life....confused,
Bitter, grimed, diseased, obsolete....
My clean, modern clothes and full stomach
Remind me of my sanity and involvement with life.
But we are all moving towards the freedom
Of nonentity and they are the nearest to it.

© Robert Morgan 1967

Discussion

1. What do you think the poet's attitude is to the people he observes?
2. Why does the poet need to be reminded of his sanity?
3. What is the freedom they are all moving towards?

Drama and Written Work

Create an improvisation based on this poem. Add other characters who might be present.

Work in a small group. One of you is a photographer and one of you is a reporter writing a piece for the Sunday papers. The others are homeless people. Interview several people on the station and write and illustrate your article.

■ THE CITY

Business men with awkward hips
And dirty jokes upon their lips
And large behinds and jingling chains,
And riddled teeth and riddling brains,
And plump white fingers made to curl
Round some anaemic city girl,
And so lead colour to their lives
And old suspicions of their wives.
Young men who wear on office stools
The ties of minor public schools,
Each learning how to be a sinner
And tell "a good one" after dinner,
And so discover it is rather
Fun to go one more than father,
But father, son and clerk join up
To talk about the Football Cup.

John Betjeman

Discuss this poem in relation to Nicky's father. How many connections can you find. By the end of the play, how has Mr Morrison changed? How do you imagine his and Nicky's relationship will be in the future?

■ Write your own poem, rap or song about living on the street.

The great escapers

by Damon Syson

When I was five, I ran away. I only made it to the bushes at the bottom of the road but I sat there for what seemed like hours, until I felt I had "punished" my father enough. I then returned triumphantly, vowing that I would give him "one more chance".

According to a recent report by the National Children's Home, 100,000 children run away every year. The vast majority are in the 14-16 age group but, as adult and streetwise as they may feel, while they are "out", they are extremely vulnerable.

Although more children run away from care than from home, the report found that 23 per cent ran from their families – many from stable, well-off families. Most stay close to home but, according to Chris Dray of the Missing Persons Bureau, an ever-increasing number are heading for large cities – putting themselves at risk of drug addiction, petty crime and prostitution. "If you haven't eaten for four days," Dray says, "and someone offers you money for sex, the temptation becomes very real."

As the Bureau's "streetworker", Dray regularly comes into contact with runaway teenagers; in some cases, he says, they do it simply for adventure. The Bureau tackled one case in which two 13-year-old girls went missing for a month. They had obtained false IDs, were living in a flat in London and claiming money from the DSS. When found, they said they'd run away "for a dare". On another occasion, Dray came across a group of children begging in Leicester Square. They had come to London "for a laugh" and couldn't get home. The youngest was five.

However, a number of the Bureau's cases follow a pattern, with runaways giving as their motive parental pressure to "do well". Three weeks ago, for example, a nationwide search was set up for student Sam Fox, 20, who went missing because she couldn't face telling her parents she had been thrown out of Swansea University. Her father, summing up the tightrope act all parents face, was reported as

saying: "We encouraged her to be herself and we didn't put her under any undue pressure – but obviously we want her to do well."

Educational psychologist Margaret McAllister believes parents have a tendency to try to "live vicariously through their children, treating them as appendages rather than as individuals". She feels poor communication is often to blame when children run away: "in their halting, inarticulate way, these children are desperately trying to get a message across. "So many parents," she adds, "experience their first problems when their children reach adolescence. They say to me, 'I don't understand it, we used to get on so well but he's turned against me. I don't recognise him any more'. The chances are, they've been talking at their children all that time rather than listening to them. The lines of communication should be established at a pre-school level; from 10 on, it becomes harder."

Despite a fear of facing their families, the majority of runaways are reunited with them within 48 hours. "Often", Chris Dray says, "they just don't know how to make that first call; they're scared they'll be shouted at. All it takes is for them to realise that people actually care and are looking for them. In my experience, they are usually very relieved to see their parents again.

The Missing Persons Bureau is on 081 392 2000

Shona's Story

Shona is a bright, normal 15 year old. She lives in a quiet town in Hampshire and is studying for GCSEs. Her background is stable and happy, yet in March of this year (when she was still 14), she ran away from home and was missing for five days. This is how she views the incident – and how her father, Murray, sees it.

I was going through a rough patch at the time, in one of those "teenage attitude" phases. The teachers would hassle me all day at school, then I'd get more hassle at home. After a while I just thought, "I can't cope with this, I've got to get out of here". My best friend Clare [not her real name] was also going through problems and we talked about running away together.

We had planned it for about two weeks. I told my parents I was going shopping on Saturday and would stay at Clare's house that night, so I had the whole weekend before anyone would be looking for me. We had £170 between us, from our savings, and we thought we were really rich. But it goes so quickly. On the train up to Waterloo, I felt like I was going on an adventure. I remember thinking, "Wow – independence".

The first night, we ended up in Islington. We found this kind of scout hut, down an alleyway.

Even though we were both wearing six jumpers and seven pairs of socks, it was freezing. We stayed in a bed and breakfast the next night and the next two days at Heathrow. During the day, I went through the Evening Standard looking for jobs. I actually went to a few interviews and was offered a job in a hairdressing salon.

The nights were fine at Heathrow, though we did get chatted up by these two men, which was a bit scary. They told us they owned a pizza parlour and kept asking us to go to a casino in Hounslow. They just wouldn't leave us alone.

Finally, on the Wednesday, we were caught by a Juvenile Protection Unit officer at Victoria Station - and he called my parents. It was a real shock when I found out how many people had been looking for me. Up to that moment, it never really hit me that what I was doing was wrong, then I suddenly thought, "God, what have I done?"

We had no idea anything was wrong until Sunday evening. Then the other girl's mother phoned, asking if she was with us, so we realised they had lied. We'd always given our daughters a lot of freedom, so I was angry that Shona had betrayed our trust.

We knew there had been an all-night party she'd wanted to go to a few miles away, so I

68

went down to the station and waited for every train. I was preparing myself for one of those, "Where the hell have been? Get in the car!" scenes, but after six or seven trains, I understood it had gone beyond that. We rang all Shona's friends but no one had seen her, so I called the police.

It was a horrible time. You go through all the emotions you'd expect: anger at the child, anger at yourself for allowing things to get to that stage. We kept asking ourselves: "What did we do wrong?" So when we got the call to pick Shona up, we didn't really know how we should act. I asked the Juvenile Protection Unit Officer what he thought and he said: "When she walks into the room, you'll just know." And we did.

She burst into tears when she saw us. We had a sort of three-way cuddle and started to talk. We talked non-stop for six hours – in a way, we haven't stopped talking since.

from the *Guardian*, June 1993

Discussion

- What reasons does the article give for why children run away?

- Why did Shona run away?

- How easy do you think it would be to survive on your own if you ran away from home?

Shona leaves home

1 Arguing
Organisation: In groups of three create a role play of Shona and her parents.

Situation: Improvise the scene which finally makes Shona decide to leave home.

First line (Father): **It's just not good enough, Shona.**

2 Planning
Organisation: Work in pairs. Shona and her friend.

Situation: You are planning to run away. Decide on the best time to go, what you take with you, where you'll head for, etc.

First line (Friend): **I've been thinking about trying to get away.**

3 Discovering

Organisation: Work in pairs as Shona's parents.

Situation: You have just discovered Clare's absence.

First line (Mother): **I've just spoken to Clare's parents. Shona's not there, and Clare's missing too.**

4 Returning

Organisation: Work in threes as Shona and her parents.

Situation: The police have found Shona and you meet for the first time since she ran away.

Going round the class, each person should contribute a different first line. Each group of three then chooses one line to develop.

REASONS FOR LEAVING

Read the extract below entitled 'Runaways'. In a large group, set up a conference about child runaways. The group is made up of professionals involved in different aspects of care, such as social workers, youth workers, drugs counsellors, etc. The teacher could be in role as a Police Liaison Officer learning why young people leave home and what recommendations the professionals can make.

Runaways

A 'runaway' is not the same as a young homeless person. A 'runaway' is someone who is away without consent. A young person under 16 cannot live legally on an independent basis, she or he is either a runaway who happens to be homeless, or a 'throwaway' – someone who has been thrown out by their parents or carers. In England and Wales the years 16 to 17 are a 'grey area', since, while parents have the right to refuse to allow a child to leave home, this right is hard to enforce. A 16 or 17-year-old in England and Wales may be a runaway or throwaway, or homeless. In Scotland a 16-year-old can leave home legally with or without parental consent.

Major research carried out by NCH, the Metropolitan Police and the Police Foundation, based on analysis of 17,000 police missing-person forms drawn from 5 Police Forces across Britain, found that:

- An estimated 43,000 young people aged 17 and under run away annually in England and Scotland and are reported missing to the police, generating over 100,000 annual reported runaway incidents.

- The numbers of boys and girls in the study who run away were roughly equal, and more than two-thirds of reported runaways were aged 14 -16. Only 7 per cent of reported runaways were of primary school age.

- 30 per cent of reported runaways in the study were running from care, overwhelmingly (96 per cent) from residential care. In comparison, fewer than 1 per cent of the same-age population are in care.

- 65 per cent of reported runaways ran away only once during the year, the remaining 35 per cent ran repeatedly, accounting for 73 per cent of all reported runaway incidents in the study. Most of these repeat runaway incidents were attributable to runaways from residential care: 62 per cent of runaways from residential care ran away more than once compared with 23 per cent of runaways from home.

- Residential care establishments in the study with apparently similar client groups had very different runaway records: runaway incidents from just 40 of them accounted for 58 per cent of all runaway incidents from care in the research.

- Contrary to popular belief, most runaways are away only quite briefly (62 per cent of runaway incidents lasted less than 24 hours), stay in their home areas (98 per cent remained locally) and return of their own accord (69 per cent).

- Despite the stereotype that London is the mecca for runaways, the study found that only 1 per cent of runaways from outside London headed for the Capital.

The NCH Factfile 1993

Discussion

If someone cannot or will not live at home, or with friends or with relatives, what can they do?

People who live in squats are breaking the law. What are the alternatives if you are under eighteen (a minor) or do not earn enough money to rent somewhere to live?

If you live on the streets, what are the problems you are likely to encounter? What dangers does Nicky face?

There have always been vagrants, tramps, nomads and gypsies who prefer not to live in houses or in settled communities. Why do you think some people prefer not to have settled homes. What would the advantages be? 'Houses box you in. They make you soft. Man was meant to live in the open air.' How far do you agree with this statement?

Debating

Conduct a debate between an invited audience with a variety
of different views and a panel comprising a young homeless
person, the Minister for Housing, the owner of a local (empty)
office block and the Head of Social Services. You may need to
ask your teacher to be an impartial chairperson.

Written Work

Write a Missing Person Profile of someone you know, or
perhaps of a celebrity. It should not be too long. Try to think
of the unique aspects of the person you are describing. You
could try reading these out in class to see if they are readily
identifiable.

In groups, plan a newspaper that would help publicise the
plight of the homeless and of runaways. What would it
contain in terms of information? What tone should it take?
What would it look like? Who would it be aimed at? Can you
come up with another method of communication that would
be more effective?

FURTHER ACTIVITIES

1. Plan a TV documentary on homelessness in the the 1990s.
   Perhaps you can actually get access to a video camera and
   create the documentary.

   Before beginning, consider the following points:
   Whose viewpoint do you want to put across? Is it
   important for the documentary to be sympathetic to one
   party, or can you devise a balanced view? Should you just
   interview people living on the streets, or include people
   who come across them casually, such as commuters or
   volunteers running the soup kitchens. Some of you could
   play the roles of council employees responsible for housing,
   the local MP, or the Minister for Housing ,and be
   interviewed by other class members. Use some of the
   characters you've developed or taken from the play to
   build up your documentary.

   Come up with a list of possible locations and write a script
   to link your interviews.

2. Research the problem of runaways and homelessness in your area. Your local council should be able to provide figures. Try and discover how much empty housing stock there is - private and council owned. How much empty office space is there? Write a letter to your local MP describing your observations on homelessness and outlining your own suggestions on how to address the problem.

3. Why are more people living on the streets of Britian then ever before?

   Try and trace the historical roots of the problem. Maybe you can plot a graph of homelessness against political events in the UK and see if there are links. Inflation, unemployment or other social or political factors will be relevant.

INFORMATION

Advisory Service For Squatters. Tel: 071-359 8814

The Big Issue, 4 Albion Place, Galena Road, London W6 OLT. Tel: 081-741 8090.

Blue Triangle. Tel: 041-332 8365

Centrepoint Soho, 140a Gloucester Mansions, Cambridge Circus, London, WC2H 8HD. Tel: 071-379 3466

CHAR, Campaign For Housing Single People, 5-15 Cromer Street, London WC1H 8LS. Tel: 071- 833 2071

Shelter, 88 Old Street, London EC1V 9HU. Tel: 071-253 0202.